Make a Difference
A Guidebook for Person-Centered Direct Support

John O'Brien and Beth Mount

with contributions by Peter Leidy and Bruce Blaney

The Everyday Heroes Quilt

Capacity Works

PO Box 271

Amenia, NY 12501-0271

888.840.8578

(In New York State: 845.373.4218)

www.capacityworks.com

Inclusion Press

24 Thome Crescent

Toronto, Ontario M6H 2S5

416.658.5363

www.inclusion.com

Library and Archives Canada Cataloguing in Publication

O'Brien, John, 1946-

    Make a difference : a guidebook for person-centred direct support / John O'Brien,
Beth Mount.

ISBN 1-895418-62-3

    1. Developmentally disabled--Services for. 2. Developmentally disabled--Counseling of.

I. Mount, Beth II. Title.

RC570.O27 2005   362.196'8   C2005-904842-5

Preparation of this publication was partially supported through a subcontract to Responsive Systems Associates from the Center on Human Policy, Syracuse University for the Research and Training Center on Community Living. The Research and Training Center on Community Living is supported through a cooperative agreement (number H133B031116) between the National Institute on Disability & Rehabilitation Research (NIDRR) and the University of Minnesota Institute on Community Integration. Members of the Center are encouraged to express their opinions; these do not necessarily represent the official position of NIDRR.

Contents

Worksheets

Diagrams

How to Use This Guidebook

Good direct support makes an important difference in the lives of people with developmental disabilities and their families. We have written this guidebook for direct support workers themselves and for the people who manage or help direct support workers, whether they are people with disabilities and family members who hire and supervise their own staff, or agency managers, or service brokers. We think that people who make policies that affect direct service work can learn something from this book too.

The more people can act on a a common understanding of the contributions that good direct support workers can make, the better the lives of people who count on direct support workers will be and the more rewarding direct service will be to workers.

You can learn something by reading the book. You will learn more if you do the exercises in the book, especially if you take the learning journey outlined in the last chapter. You will learn even more if you are part of a learning group. A learning group can be a formal class or a group of three or four who gather around a kitchen table. What matters is having people who can share your thoughts and experiences.

We would be very glad to know about how you have used this guidebook and to hear any suggestions you might have for making the book better. Contact us at inclusionpress@inclusion.com.

Thanks for reviewing and improving this book to Connie Lyle O'Brien, Kim Turner, Brian Salisbury, Lynda Kahn, Jack Pearpoint, Jack Pealer, David Pitonyak, Alan Tyne, Mary Romer, and Pam Walker.

How You Make a Difference

As a direct support worker you can choose to make a positive difference in the lives of the people you assist. If you choose to make a positive difference, you will join the direct support workers you will meet in this book. These workers deserve to be called "Everyday Heroes" because, day after day, they support people with disabilities to act as full citizens who make a worthwhile contribution to their communities. Direct support work is seldom glamorous and it is not a way to become rich in money, but it can be important and it can be rich in human relationships if you decide to make it so.

This book comes from what we have learned from direct support workers as they step back from the busy-ness of their work and ask themselves, **"When we are at our very best, what works to improve the lives of the people we support?"** and **"What makes our work worth doing?"** The ideas and activities you find in this guidebook have met this test: direct support workers, people with disabilities, and family members have used them and found them helpful.

The fact that people became heroes and sheroes can be credited to their ability to identify and empathize with the "other." These men and women could continue to live quite comfortably with their slow temperament but they chose not to. They made the decision to be conscious of the other –the homeless, the downtrodden and the oppressed. Heroism has nothing to do with skin color or social status. It is a state of mind and a willingness to act for what is right and just.

–Maya Angelou

When they think about their work and how it makes a difference, effective direct support workers agree on one basic idea. **When it is done well, the work engages our hearts, our minds and our hands,** as this symbol reminds us.

You make a difference by building a relationship that supports a person to act as a contributing citizen.

It's how you look at your work that makes the difference. If you look at it as just a list of personal care tasks and household chores for clients who really don't have much to offer, there isn't so much room for pride in your work. If you look at your job as the chance to make a positive relationship with people who can offer a lot if they have the right support, then you find your reason to work right there with the people themselves.

–Direct Support Worker

You don't make a positive difference by simply showing up and doing a list of assigned chores. You don't make a positive difference by just going through the motions of following policies and procedures. You make a positive difference by bringing yourself to the tasks and requirements of your work. Your courage, your creativity, your wisdom, your knowledge, your commitment make the difference when you meet the heart and mind of the person you support.

The first step is to choose to do your work in a way that makes a positive difference in the lives of the people you assist. No one can order you to do this, because it is the way you are with people that makes the difference. You can keep learning every day how to be more effective with people. Training sessions can help, being part of an effective staff team helps a lot, but this learning begins inside you and happens between you and the person you support. No one can teach you what you need to know about building a good relationship unless you decide to learn by acting and reflecting.

The way you are with people makes the difference.

- The person counts on you
- You have time to get to know the person
- You accompany the person into new experiences
- You may earn the person's trust

Your most important choices are the ones that shape your relationships with the people you assist. There are at least four things about the work you do that give you the chance to build a relationship that makes a positive difference.

The person counts on you for the assistance they need to keep their life going. You may help the person understand and connect with what is happening in the world around them. You may help other people understand what the person wants them to know. You may help a person to wash, get dressed, eat, and use the toilet. You may help a person sit comfortably in their wheelchair and use their communication device. You may help a person keep their home clean and fix their meals. You may help a person do what they need to do to be secure and well.

People can get into real difficulties, and for some people that happens a lot. The way I spend time with people when things are ok builds up a relationship that makes it easier to defuse difficult situations.

– Direct Support Worker

You may help a person get where they want to go and look great when they get there. You may help a person pay their bills and read their mail. You may help a person to meet their employer's requirements for a job well done. You may play an important part in helping people learn things that matter to them. If you choose to do these everyday tasks reliably, respectfully and thoughtfully, you will provide the person with a strong foundation for their life.

You can get to know a lot about a person if you are looking and listening to them while you do routine stuff. The better you know someone, the better you understand them. The better you understand someone, the easier it is to deal with the parts of their personality that are not likable. It makes a kind of positive circle. The work parts of the job are easier the better you know the person you are helping.

–Direct Support Worker

A woman with cerebral palsy used her letterboard to spell out this message. She communicates the difference it makes when a direct support worker does everyday tasks with respect and attention. She also provides a window on her side of the relationship by telling us about the work she does in order to receive physical assistance.

If I could, I would give each staff person a gift. I would give them the gift of feeling what it is like for me to get up in the morning and get ready for the day. They know it from their side; they know what it's like to do the work of helping me shower and get dressed. But I want them to feel the work it takes from my side to get the help. It takes a lot of energy from me and I can tell, by the person's touch, whether they care anything about my day or not. When you matter to the person helping you, this work of getting help is not so tiring.

You have time to get to know the person by sharing everyday experiences with them, including times of crisis or troubles. If you choose to converse and listen and observe with interest, over time you will learn important things about who the person is and what really matters to them. Your interest will encourage the person. It may also help the person become more clear about what they want from life and more confident in their ability to get more of the good things that they want.

You accompany the person as they meet new people and experiences. If you look at new situations –whether a trip to the beach or a trip to the hospital– through the eyes of the person you are assisting, you can often spot ways to improve the odds that the person will be as comfortable as possible, look good, make a positive impression, and benefit from the experience.

> Sometimes it doesn't feel like a job at all. Sometimes I think, "I can't believe I get paid for just being with people and helping them live their lives."
>
> – Direct Support Worker

If you are interested in the person, and careful in providing assistance, and you stick with the person, you may **earn the person's trust** and become a sounding board and adviser. You may also become an important part of planning and decision-making if family members and other team members come to trust your place in the person's life.

The focus of this book

This book offers you a way to learn how to do your work even better than you do now by taking a learning journey with a person with a developmental disability.

There are many important skills to learn and practice if you are to fulfill your responsibility to provide good assistance. You may need to know how to lift a person safely, or how to help a person to eat comfortably, or how to assist a person to establish self-control, or how to teach something a person finds difficult to learn. This book does not try to teach you these kinds of skills for three reasons.

- You need to be skillful in doing exactly what the person you assist needs done in the way that works best for them. This means you need to learn from people who know exactly what this person needs and wants from you. Almost always, the person who needs assistance can teach you much of what you need to know about how to assist them, whether they use words or not. Others who know the person well –experienced support workers, family members, friends– will be able to show you exactly what works. Some procedures, like administering medications, may need to be taught or supervised by a licensed professional.

- Skills are best learned by watching someone do what you need to learn and then practicing with supervision until you are competent and confident. When specialized knowledge is required, it needs to be taught by experts who can test and build your understanding as you learn by doing. This is the way professionals like surgeons and nurses and psychologists learn their practical skills; this is the way you should learn your practical skills.

Your courage, your creativity, your wisdom, your knowledge, your commitment make the difference when you meet the heart and mind of the person you support.

- Direct support workers are not junior therapists or junior nurses. You have your own contribution to make to people's lives. You

One of Your Stories About Making a Positive Difference

Think about a time when you made a positive difference in the life of a person you assist (it doesn't have to be a big difference, just a difference you feel good about making). Describe what you did and what happened for the person.

Write down your ideas about exactly what you did that made that positive difference.

What was it about this that made you feel good about making this difference?

Good direct support encourages each person in the relationship to be all that they can be.

make your contribution by building a relationship that supports a person to act as a contributing citizen. This support includes providing the assistance a person needs in a skillful way, but it is more than that. Support is a relationship that encourages each person in the relationship to be all that they can be. We want this book to encourage you in the relationship dimension of your work.

This is a guide book to greater ability to make a positive difference. You can learn something by just reading the book, and more by using the worksheets, but the best way to learn is to work with a partner who has a developmental disability and explore new opportunities for community contribution. You will learn about how to make change by working on a change with your partner, reflecting on your efforts to identify important lessons, and reporting what you are learning.

The way your job is structured influences how much you can contribute to the lives of the people you support and how much you can learn from using this guidebook. The worksheet on the next page lets you assess how well your job supports you to make a positive difference.

This is the roadmap for your learning journey.

Make an agreement to learn together →

Try something new in the community
- Organize information
- Make a plan
- Make connections
- Adjust assistance as needed

Ask "What's working?"

Ask "How do we build on what's working?"

Ask "What are we learning?"

Tell the story of what you are learning

How Well Does Your Workplace Support Your Contribution?

Use this checklist to describe the support your workplace gives to building powerful relationships with the people you assist. Conditions that rate below "3" call for negotiation with your supervisor if you are going to get the most out of using this guide book.

Harder to build a powerful relationship when…		**Easier** to build a powerful relationship when…
I get pulled from place to place or reassigned too often to get to know people very well or work on change with them for very long.	1_____3_____5	I have a stable assignment with people I can get to know and work with on making positive changes in their lives.
I have to work so many hours that I am often too tired to be involved in making change with people.	1_____3_____5	My workload is reasonable. I have time and energy to be involved in making change with people.
I have so many tasks to do that there is no time left for just be-ing with people or working on a change with them.	1_____3_____5	I have a good balance of assigned tasks that gives me time to be with the people I assist and work for change with them.
I am assigned to so many people that I can't really get to know any-one very well.	1_____3_____5	The number of people I assist makes it easy to get to know people.
My supervisor discourages me from getting to know the people I assist or working on changes outside the usual routine.	1_____3_____5	My supervisor values my rela-tionships with the people I assist and encourages me to work for changes that matter to people.
I don't feel like I belong to a team that supports me in my relation-ships with the people I assist and in making changes with them.	1_____3_____5	I belong to a strong team that actively supports my relationships and positive actions with the people I assist.

Can I do it?

Some direct support workers feel uncertain about accepting responsibility for working on a change with a person they assist. We encourage you to listen to what your uncertainty is telling you and try it anyway. Use the voice of your uncertainty to make a smarter try at the change. Many direct support workers have moved through their uncertainties to greater skill and satisfaction.

- **"The people I assist don't want to change. I'd be imposing on them."** You are not imposing a change, you are asking a person to help you learn something that will make you better at your work by helping them to get more of something that is important to them. We have found that very few people say no, if you ask sincerely and respectfully. If you strengthen your relationship by sharing your time and listening carefully, many people will discover a change worth trying to make.

- **"I don't know how."** That is the reason that you are taking the time to learn. The only way to learn is to try, test what's working and what's not, and try another way –over and over again.

- **"I'm not creative."** That statement is only true as long as your belief in it keeps you from trying. Everyone we have worked with who is willing to move a little outside their comfort zone discovers that they are plenty creative enough to learn something useful and interesting.

- **"I will only be able to make a tiny change."** Many direct support workers have demonstrated that "one good thing leads to another" as long as you notice a positive change, however small, and follow the direction that the change indicates. No change is too small, as long as it leads to a positive next step.

- **"I might fail."** Maybe. As long as you don't put the person in danger, failing can be part of learning. At any rate, the person will not fail alone. If you fail, you will fail together, and you will be able to identify the lessons of failure and try again.

There is only one reason not to try: if you cannot find a partner that you like. If you dislike a potential partner, talk your dislike over with someone you trust. Do not do the activities in this book unless you can honestly say that you want to change your way of being with the person in order to have a better relationship with them and assist them to get more of the good things in life.

What You Want For People Is Powerful

Read the research findings summarized in the box.

> Researchers following-up on the quality of life for young people with complex support needs who moved out of an institution identified a number of areas where quality needs improvement, especially around support for choice, involvement in community life, and dealing with difficult behavior. They asked about training for direct support staff. Most staff received 20-40 hours of required training when hired and 10-20 hours of training a year while at work. The researchers found that...
>
> ... 100% of direct support workers said "Yes" when asked if they have sufficient training to offer high quality support.
>
> ... 100% of managers say "Yes" when asked if direct support staff have sufficient training to offer high quality support.
>
> ... 60% of family members say "Yes" when asked if staff have sufficient training to offer high quality support.
>
> ... 35% of family members say they don't know staff well enough to judge the quality of their training.
>
> As the researchers thought about what their findings mean, they said:
>
> ..."The greatest barrier to training is the belief that additional training is not needed."
>
> ..."If people do not have a vision of a life for people with substantial disabilities that includes work, friends, meaningful days, important community roles, and exercising choice and control, then those people will not see the need for training that will help them to have the skills to make this vision a reality."
>
> – Stoneman, Z., & Al-Deen, B. (1999). Rivers Crossing -- *Transition from institution to the Community.* Athens, GA: University of Georgia, Institute on Human Development and Disability.

List the main reasons you think staff would say they have enough training, even though there are important quality problems.	List your main reasons for agreeing or disagreeing with the researchers about the connection between vision for people and desire for training.	What other information would help you be more sure about your reasons?
•	•	•
•	•	•
•	•	•

Make a Choice For Learning

Write down what **you** most want to learn by using this guidebook.

> We only truly live by knowing; otherwise we simply perform, copying the daily habits of others, but conceiving nothing of our creative possibilities as humans.
>
> –Alice Walker

Have Courage
See with the Eyes of the Heart

I and i feel like you do

How could you look in my eyes and abuse me
How could you look in my eyes and refuse me
This is my life not a movie
This is not news for the TV
Cho.

I and i feel pain like you do
I and i feel anger like you do
I and i feel sadness like you do
And I and i feel joy too
I and i need loving like you do
I and i need greetings like you do
I and i need the same things like you do
So treat i like I treat you

Such a thin line between love and hate
So patience and compassion i celebrate
What i can't control i appreciate
And everything else will fall in place
The things people do to me make little sense
Like being discriminated against
But what they don't know i'll never be bent
i persevere through my resilience
Cho.

i don't know why i am the way i am
i didn't ask to be the way i am
All i know: i am the way i am
And i am a lot more than what they say i am
All i ever wanted was the right
To do what ever i like
Have the opportunities to make the choice
To do the things that empower my life
Cho.

So now you know me
i hope a little love you'll show me
This is my story
And to the most high be the glory
How could you look in my eyes and abuse me
How could you look in my eyes and refuse me
This is my life not a movie
This is not news for the TV

–Rohan Robinson
Direct Support Worker

20

Keys to a satisfying job

Many people think of your work as little more than babysitting for people that no one else wants to be around. To them it seems like a job for a saint or a job for people who can't find anything else or a job that someone might do while waiting for a better opportunity to come along. This attitude of disrespect for the people you assist and for your work is often reflected in low pay and poor working conditions. In many places, waiting on tables offers better pay and benefits than assisting a person with a disability.

Everyone who cares about a good life for people with disabilities needs to do the political work necessary to win fair wages, adequate benefits, and decent working conditions for direct support workers.

But this political work can take a long time and the victories are more often small pay increases rather than big leaps in people's understanding of and respect for the work you do. In the meantime, you may find yourself in a place where you feel overwhelmed and disconnected from the positive possibilities in the work.

In a way, the low value that society places on the work can get inside your head and tempt you to disrespect yourself. You can get stuck in a vicious circle: you feel powerless and mistreated and so you do the least work you can get away with, so you accomplish very little with the people you support, and so you feel little pride in your work. When you meet with your supervisors or attend training you tune out. When you spend time with your co-workers you talk about what's wrong but don't figure out how to take action to make things better. The job makes you feel mistreated, resentful, and powerless to do anything about it.

This is an uhappy and dangerous place to be. The people with disabilities who count on you have to make do with poor support from people who disrespect themselves. You miss the real rewards of building good relationships and making a positive difference.

There are at least three ways to avoid getting stuck in this trap.

First, you can figure out how to **advocate for better lives for yourself and the people you support.** As Rohan's song shows, both you and the people you support deserve respect. Claiming that respect takes real courage.

Danger Signs

You are overwhelmed: you feel mistreated, resentful, and powerless to do anything about it.

What To Do

• Advocate

• Invest yourself in positive changes for the people you support

• Build a strong team and a positive organization

For ways to speak out for a better deal for direct support workers, visit **The National Alliance for Direct Support Professionals** at www.nadsp.org.

Second, you can **refuse to act like a low paid babysitter for people of little worth**. You can decide to invest yourself in your work in ways that assist people with developmental disabilities to become better known to other people as contributing community members. This will make a positive change in public attitudes as people with disabilities educate more and more people through direct contact with them. Doing the activities in this book will help you improve your ability to do this.

Third, you can **help build up a strong team and a positive organization**. One important way to do this is to mentor new direct support workers. Most new workers take their cues from other, more experienced workers. Because what you do speaks very loudly, to be a good mentor you first need to be a good model. It also helps to have a clear understanding of what a worker has to be willing to do in order to make the job meaningful.

The advice that a group of experienced direct support workers* want to give their new co-workers is on the following pages. Their thoughts are organized by the image of signposts that guide a journey toward meaningful work.

Identify Star Quotes

As you read the next section, look for quotations from these workers that ring a bell in you and put a star next to each one. Pick one or two of your star quotes and put them on a card to carry in your day planner or stick on your refrigerator. Show one of your star quotes to a co-worker or fellow student and talk about what it says to you and how you can build on its message to make you better able to make a difference to the people you support.

* Thanks to direct support workers from Creative Community Living Services, South Central Region, Madison, Wisconsin for discussing this topic in December 2003.

I slept and dreamed that life was joy.

I awoke and saw that life was service

I served and understood that service was joy

–Rabindranath Tagore

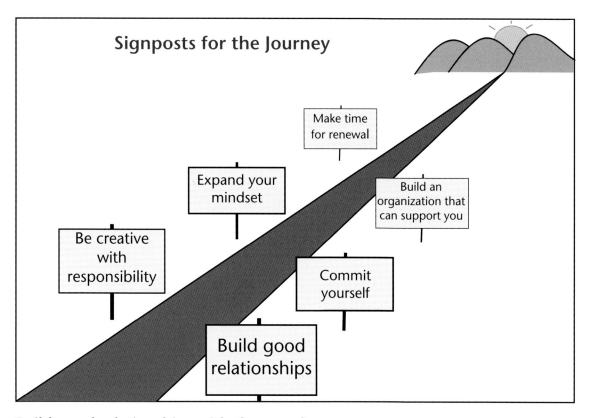

Signposts for the Journey

- Make time for renewal
- Expand your mindset
- Build an organization that can support you
- Be creative with responsibility
- Commit yourself
- Build good relationships

Build good relationships with the people you support

Attachment to people is the way to satisfaction in the work.

§

Talk and listen to people as equals. Don't talk down to people.

§

Putting the person first rather than putting yourself first doesn't make you inferior, and it doesn't mean you have to act like a doormat. It means that you remember that you are there to support a person to have a satisfying life. Remember, you are coming into their home. In lots of situations you need to be the one who adjusts and adapts to the person before expecting the person to adapt to your ways of doing things.

§

Even if you've known someone a long time, don't presume too much, especially when you are predicting how the person will respond to new experiences. People can respond to new opportunities differently –and lots of times better– than you think they will.

§

Build good relationships

Allow people time and room to develop.

§

Each of our lives has ups and downs, ebbs and flows. People need us to stick with them through all that they experience.

§

Talk through annoyances; don't let them build up and poison your relationships.

§

Believe that people who don't use words can think, and want to communicate with you.

§

There will be times that you will anger, or disappoint, or hurt each other. Find ways to get through them. Asking forgiveness helps.

§

Keep finding out more about people by listening to them and by listening to people who know them in other ways (like family members or staff from a long time ago).

Be thoughtful and creative with responsibility

Be creative with responsibility

Being the responsible person doesn't mean controlling. Notice and count on the person's competencies. You don't have to be the "alpha cat".

§

Listening and figuring out how to assist people to have what they really want in their lives is the most important job.

§

Our job is to assist people, not run people's lives. Respect and a good relationship are the foundation for being responsible for another person's health and safety.

§

Just because people need support or structure for decision making doesn't mean you get to take over. It's easy to impose the first solution you can think of. And it can be hard to let go of your solution if a person doesn't go along with it. People react badly to having their choices taken over. And lots of people don't like being told "it's for your own good" with no other information. Find ways to guide people in thinking for themselves.

§

Build on what people do know and can do. Everybody can participate in some way.

§

Look for ways to balance situations rather than taking over. Sometimes it's you (or the schedule) that needs to have something done now. Find ways to negotiate these situations: "If you help me do this now, then I will…"

§

People's desires and opinions matter. If something seems really important to a person but you don't agree, take time to ask a couple of questions before you react with "no". Can you and the person find some other way to get what the person wants that is safer or more acceptable? What is the potential harm: is this really dangerous for the person or just inconvenient for me?

Commit yourself

Give yourself to the people you support and the situations you find yourself in.

§

Expect, embrace, and enjoy challenges. See yourself as a cooperative problem solver.

§

Look for ways to use your strengths, talents, and interests on behalf of the people you support.

§

Work on increasing your flexibility by learning new skills.

§

Make sure this is what you want to be doing. Decide: "This is where I belong."

§

Commit yourself

Help people find goals that are really important to them and encourage and assist people to move toward them.

Expand your mindset and check your attitude

Your attitude can change almost anything. You always have some control over how you take what's happening to you.

§

Don't be surprised if you discover prejudices in yourself; prejudice is common in our society. Do be willing to re-think and find ways to change your experience of the people you hold a prejudice about whether they are people with disabilities or family members, or other staff.

§

Keep an open mind, especially about what good things are possible for the people you support.

§

Look for positives, especially when you are feeling down or cynical. They are there.

§

Notice when you are on autopilot –just going through the motions of the job. If this lasts very many days, it's a sign that you need to re-energize.

§

Be open to give-and-take. You can be both a learner and a teacher.

§

See the people you support as important teachers. Ask yourself: "What have I learned from this person lately?"

§

Keep finding ways to look differently at difference. Some differences that seem negative or undesirable are abilities in disguise. Some abilities are hidden behind labels and low expectations.

§

Don't get stuck in the impossible mission of saving the world.

§

Don't get stuck in the self-defeating belief that nothing you do can make a difference.

§

See how quickly you can catch yourself making negative assumptions about the people you support, about yourself, about your organization. See how many ways you can find to check out and disprove those negative assumptions.

Make time for renewal

Take time away when you need it. Sometimes a time as short as a couple of minutes can be enough. Sometimes you need a much longer break.

§

Renew by thinking about what you are learning from your work.

§

Use some of your time to reflect. You can do this in conversation with others or just in your own mind.

§

There are lots of different kinds of satisfactions in the work. Look for new ones.

§

Don't be afraid to step back and think about your work.

§

Make time for your feelings and for reflecting on your feelings, especially after something upsetting or very difficult has happened that you have had to stay on top of while it was happening.

§

If you find yourself feeling isolated, ask yourself: 1) how can I bring my relationship with the people I support alive? 2) Who can I reach out to among my co-workers or managers?

§

Look back over what you have been doing and ask, "If it was me, or my sister, or my father getting what I have given over the past week, how would I feel about it? What would I have wanted done different?"

Build an organization that can support your work

Find co-workers to trust. The best way to build trust is to be trustworthy: do what you say you will do and tell the truth.

§

Stop to notice and appreciate co-worker's and manager's investment in people.

§

Don't do it alone. Back up is available. If you are scared, or stumped, or stuck you can get help from managers and co-workers. Don't be afraid to say, "I don't know." or "I've made a mistake."

§

Sometimes a match just doesn't work. Instead of just quitting, ask for help. It doesn't have to be a matter of blame –for you or forthe person. Maybe there are different ways for you to approach the relationship. Maybe you would work very effectively with a different person.

§

Celebrate the different benefits the differences among us staff bring people. Our different ages and cultures mean we can offer different positives. People need the energy that some can bring; they also need the warmth that others can bring.

§

Watch how much time you spend in negative gossip about the people we support, about co-workers, about the organization. If there is a real problem, find a way to work on it. Negative gossip can be a killer.

Build an organization that can support you

William Britt – who lived for 34 years in institutions– created this painting to honor the direct support workers who have reached out to him throughout his life. The open hand –a symbol of human concern– represents the kindness of helpers who have touched his life along the way.

The light bulb represents the good ideas that workers bring into the lives of others and the insight gained from sharing the journey. William captures the brightness of divine imagination, and reminds us all of how human potential can blossom when nurtured by human concern.

The human figures engaged in the activities of everyday life symbolize membership for people with disabilities. With the soaring figures, William reminds us that people can rise above their limitations and fly on the supportive wings of others who care.

Ten Things I'd Like to Tell My Employer

Peter Leidy

There is much to be learned from the experiences of direct support workers. For agencies supporting people with developmental disabilities; for elected officials deciding how public money is spent; for people with disabilities and their families. If you are reading this, you are likely aware that support workers generally have low pay, low benefits, and low status. Yet they do very important work.

As more citizens previously separated from the community begin to have meaningful lives, and as options increase for individuals to move out from their family's home, we see a greater need for direct support workers. It is a happy fact that as more people with disabilities gain opportunities for individualized support to live and work in the community, more personal assistants are needed.

As agencies employing direct care staff learn to listen more closely to them, there is more reason to be hopeful about the future of community life for people with disabilities. Hearing what staff on the frontlines have to say can and should lead to better support of staff and people with disabilities.

Despite the great diversity among direct support staff, certain messages continue to rise to the surface. These recurring themes, if heard and acted upon, can result in better support to staff, a reduction in turnover, and improved quality of life for people being served. This "Top Ten" list reflects many of these themes, as heard over time from support workers in Wisconsin and elsewhere. It is not an exhaustive list, nor are the points in a particular order. (Please note: "Take this job and shove it" didn't make the top 10.)

Let's look at the list from the point of view of "Barb", a direct support worker who assists "Theresa", and what she would say to the agency she works for. They have worked together for two years, since Theresa moved out of a large facility into her own home.

1. Help me get off to a good start.

Here are some thoughts as I reflect on when I began working with Theresa, and knowing what I know now. There's a lot to absorb at the start of a new job. I need to learn about the agency, and mostly I need to learn about Theresa. And she needs to learn about me. Remember when you started – that feeling of being new? I am excited, and I am happy to have been offered this job, and I'm a bit scared. Everything is new, I have a lot of responsibility, and I want to do a good job.

I would like you to tell me all about Theresa, and give Theresa plenty of room to tell me all about herself, in whatever ways she can. I mean the things I need to know to do my job, and the things Theresa wants me to know. I don't expect Theresa's life to be an open book for me to read – after all, we're just meeting each other. But there are things I need to know, most of which are things Theresa wants me to know. What's important to her? What are the musts and the must-nots? Help me learn how these influence my required job duties, and be specific about what those duties are.

2. Be aware of my isolation.

This is a one-to-one job. I like it that way. Being able to spend time assisting Theresa and having the kind of relationship we do works for me. Most of the time, it is a satisfying way to spend my work time. But sometimes I feel pretty alone. I don't have co-workers around much. I don't often experience working with a team, even though there are others who support Theresa.

It would be nice to occasionally have get-togethers with other people who do this kind of work, to find out what it's like for them, or why they got involved doing this. Or to talk about what a great day Theresa and I just had – or what a difficult day we just had. A lot of people meet friends through work, and with direct support that can be difficult.

3. Ask for my input on issues related to my job.

As Theresa and I get to know each other better over time, I will gain some valuable insights about her. My knowledge and understanding could be useful in the support we're all providing for her. See my role over time with Theresa evolve from "Tell me what I need to know and do" in the beginning to "Let me tell you what I'm learning that we all need to know" as time goes on. I become a valuable resource for determining with you and Theresa what the agency's support should look like. Also, I begin to seek ways that I can stretch in my job – to try new things, to learn more, and to grow.

4. Communication and supervision are important to me.

There are several people directly involved with Theresa's support. We need to get together on a regular basis, both for sharing important information and for supporting each other.

As my supervisor, talk with me about supervision. It may mean something different to me than it does to you. Getting to know each other is important. Having regular contact is important. Checking in with me (rather than checking up on me) is important. Letting me know when you think things are going well, and not just when something is wrong, is important. Being available when I need to talk to you, or making sure someone else is, and getting back to me in a timely fashion when I try to reach you – these are all important.

When we do talk, I need you to hear what I'm saying. I know you're busy, and time is tight. But please listen to me. Find out what's on my mind. If you tell me you are going to do something, follow up with me about it. Let me know you did it, or whether there will be a delay. If we have not talked in a while, don't assume everything is okay. In this type of work, no news is not necessarily good news.

5. Offer training opportunities beyond what's required.

I love the blood borne pathogens training!! Who doesn't? But there are so many more learning opportunities available (or which could be developed) that would be beneficial to me. I realize resources are limited. I know that time taken away from being with Theresa means finding someone else to work with her. Still, ongoing learning experiences are important to support workers – to gain knowledge, to help me do my job better, to get rejuvenated, to meet other people.

6. I like my job and I want to keep it.

I like Theresa, and I like spending time with her. It is a good job, I do it well, and this is important to me. I don't want to work in a job that I don't like simply because I need income. I want to look forward to my job, at least most of the time, and be able to put positive energy into it. I'm telling you this because I think it's important that you know how I feel about my work. I want you to know that I want to keep doing it, because if you know I'm invested in it, there is a greater chance that you'll invest more in me, and that's good for all of us.

7. Acknowledge my work and me.

Sometimes my work is extremely challenging. Sometimes, others don't seem to believe that what I am doing is very important. There are days when it feels like no one cares that I'm here, doing my job –even Theresa. Please understand that at times I need encouragement or a pat on the back, or just someone to say, "What you do is

important and valuable." I may get messages from family, friends, society that tell me otherwise. So I need you to show me you care, that what I do makes a difference.

8. I don't get paid a fair wage.

I'm not whining; I'm stating a fact. I knew the pay when I started, and I realize it may take a long time before this changes. But what can I do, and what can Theresa do, and what will you do, to work for change? Have you worked on this issue before? If so, tell me about it.

I know it's not as simple as asking you for a raise. There is an institutional bias in this country, and community services, already underfunded, have seen cuts at state and local levels. Meanwhile, the cost of health insurance has skyrocketed. Who do I write to? Who do I call? Let's advocate together.

9. I understand the need for an organizational hierarchy, but….

All employees have a place in the hierarchy; the buck has to stop somewhere. It looks to me like my job is at the bottom of the totem pole, or darn close to it.

If there must be a hierarchy, help me to not always feel that I'm at the bottom. My position here, and the others like it, is the closest on a daily basis to people with disabilities. We're important. So, if on the organizational chart we need to be low, find ways to lift us up. Frankly, the chart doesn't matter all that much to me. What matters is how I'm treated as an employee. Consider that it may also be best for Theresa if those of us from different places on the chart work collaboratively – if we acknowledge the chain of command but don't dwell on it. If we mix it up here and there when possible. I'm not suggesting I begin telling the Executive Director what to do (though I'm not opposed to the idea!) but rather, that those of you "above" us direct support workers respect us enough to understand what the hierarchy can sometimes feel like to us.

Here is one example: I'd been working with Theresa for a year when my supervisor quit. A new coordinator was hired (with no input from me or Theresa, by the way) and began getting to know Theresa. It got a little awkward, me knowing Theresa pretty well by then and teaching my new supervisor some things, but my new supervisor telling me what to do. She needed to learn her job, which included supervising me, yet there were some things I knew more about. She had a hard time accepting that it would take her a while to learn everything she'd need to, and wanted to quickly put on the "supervisor hat." I wanted to say, "Chill out! You'll have plenty of opportunities to direct me!" But I didn't.

10. Some flexibility is good for everybody.

My flexibility is important to you, and to Theresa. The need for it is inherent in this kind of work. So many things that go on in Theresa's life rely on people to make them happen – people who, being humans, make mistakes and get stuck in traffic and get sick and oversleep.

So you ask me to be flexible, and this is reasonable. I think there are times when flexibility on your part is also needed. Not always, in every situation, no matter what. That would not be reasonable—just as it would not be reasonable for you to expect that I would be willing or able to change plans or schedules all the time. But it's worth thinking about ways in which you, my agency, and you, my supervisor, can show flexibility toward me. After all, I've been here two years now, longer than the average direct support worker. And I've done a good job. I'm reliable, I have a good relationship with Theresa, and I bring a lot to my work.

Whether it concerns my job duties, or my schedule, or a time off request—whatever it may be, please consider the circumstances. Working together, with give and take, benefits all of us: you, Theresa, and me.

Which of these ten things are especially important to you? What would you add to his list? What would you take away?

Who else do you want to discuss this paper with?

Challenge Limiting Beliefs

You make a difference by building a relationship that supports each person with a disability to act as a contributing member of their community. You build this relationship by providing people the assistance they need in ways that make sense to them and earn their trust.

Everyone, developmentally disabled or not, has to figure out how they can best contribute to community life. Contribution is an ordinary sort of thing. People contribute by what they do face-to-face, day-to-day …

…with and for their family and friends.

…with their neighbors by everyday conversations and favors and in block clubs, neighborhood associations, neighborhood watch groups, and local celebrations.

…through their jobs and with their co-workers.

…in their churches, synagogues, and mosques.

…by playing an active part in the political process.

…as members of associations like softball teams, youth organizations, theatre groups, environmental groups, and service clubs.

People with developmental disabilities travel a tougher road to community contribution than many other people do. This is because our society has not yet learned to fully value people with developmental disabilities. Though there has been real progress in the last fifty years, limiting beliefs still close off too many people from opportunities for contribution. Some of these limiting beliefs have a grain of truth inside them, but people with developmental disabilities and their allies have proved these beliefs mostly wrong. Hopeful action shows the injustice that happens when people accept these limiting beliefs and the benefits that come from challenging them.

What we believe about people with developmental disabilities shapes the opportunities we help people with disabilities to develop and the way we provide the assistance they need. The way we provide assistance shapes what people

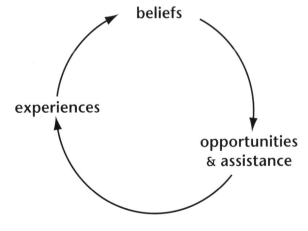

Limiting Belief About "Them"	Grain of Truth	What People with Developmental Disabilities and Their Allies Are Proving
"They can't learn or can only learn very simple things."	Some people require very capable and systematic instruction to learn as much as they can.	Almost everyone can learn some things that are meaningful to them and those who know them, and most people can learn a great deal when it matters to them.
"They are happiest when they are with their own kind. Non-disabled people won't accept them."	Many people with disabilities gather strength and enjoyment from their friendships with other disabled people and their membership in self-advocacy groups.	Many non-disabled people have good friendships with people with developmental disabilities. A growing number of employers, businesses, and community organizations are willing to make accommodations to support the involvement of people with disabilities.
"Their lives need to be supervised by medical professionals."	Like other people, people with disabilities sometimes get sick. Like many other people, some people with developmental disabilities live with chronic illnesses like asthma, diabetes or heart disease.	Impairments in sensing, processing information, learning, using language, and movement are not illnesses but ordinary human experiences. What people need is access, accommodation, and personal assistance.
"They need to be controlled. They can't make decisions because they have the minds of children in the bodies of adults."	Some people need substantial support to make decisions. Some people may have a legally appointed person to make substitute choices for them.	Almost everyone can make their preferences known if good listeners and observers are present to them. Most people can make reasonable decisions if people who believe in their ability are available to inform and support their thinking.
"Institutions and day centers are the only way to keep them safe and provide necessary services cost effectively."		People with all types of need for assistance are living, learning, working, playing in ordinary community places – sometimes with assistance and accommodation. Institutions and programs that congregate large groups of people are not necessary or cost effective for anybody.

with disabilities –and all the rest of us– experience. What we experience shapes our beliefs and the circle keeps on turning.

This circle makes limiting beliefs into confinement and liberating beliefs into community contributions. When the circle is driven by fear it increases confinement and discouragement. When the circle is driven by hope it increases contribution and courage.

Here is an example of how the beliefs–opportunities–experiences circle shaped the services we have today and how a growing number of people are reversing the negative circle and turning positive beliefs into good experiences. For many years most people believed that people with substantial difficulties in learning (people labeled "moderately mentally retarded" or "severely mentally retarded") could not be employed. The circle looked like this.

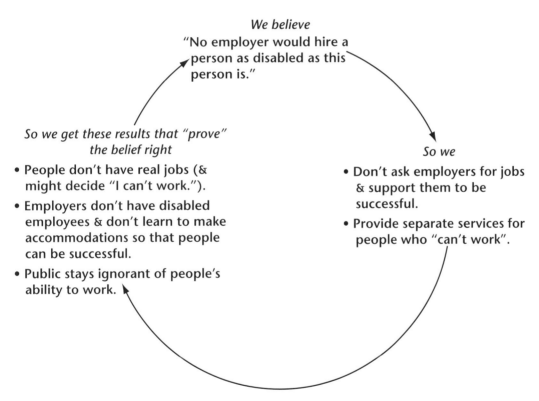

We believe
"No employer would hire a person as disabled as this person is."

So we get these results that "prove" the belief right

- People don't have real jobs (& might decide "I can't work.").
- Employers don't have disabled employees & don't learn to make accommodations so that people can be successful.
- Public stays ignorant of people's ability to work.

So we

- Don't ask employers for jobs & support them to be successful.
- Provide separate services for people who "can't work".

As long as this circle controls what we do, we will make it come true. We don't learn how to assist people to find and succeed at real jobs, so people don't have real jobs. We point to the fact that people don't have real jobs to prove that no employer would ever hire a person like this.

Stop assuming, "It can't be." Start asking, "What would it take?"

Key Word

Allies – People who commit themselves to be on your side and help you to have a good life. Family members can be allies. Friends with disabilities and friends without disabilities can be allies. Staff members can be allies. What counts is not someone's role but their follow through on their promise: "I choose to be on your side."

Allies are not slaves. Sometimes they may disagree with a person, argue with a person, even withhold their support from a person. What they will not do is walk away from the person.

Key Words

Impairment – An individual difference that results in a need for access, accommodation or assistance if the person is to function effectively in settings that matter to the person.

Disability – the disadvantage that comes from barriers which impact on people with impairments and the lack of appropriate access, accommodation, and assistance.

Limiting beliefs are especially powerful when good people accept them without questioning. When "everybody knows" that people with substantial disabilities can't work, those that a person trusts discourage the person from even thinking about a real job. This could be for what seem like good reasons: to protect the person from disappointment or failure. But it puts the limiting belief inside the person's head and shrinks the possibility of contribution through work and the rewards of a real paycheck.

Turning the circle from one that puts up barriers to one that opens up opportunities calls on a person and their allies to make a commitment to learning by taking action and reflecting on what their action teaches them. This learning starts with replacing the limiting belief with a question. They stop assuming that "No employer would hire this person." Instead, they ask "What would it take for this person to be successful at doing a real job?" This leads to more questions and to hard work on finding good answers to them.

- What kind of job, in what kind of workplace, suits this person's capacities and personal interests?
- Who hires people for jobs like that and what is the best way for this person to approach them for a job?
- Once we know where the potential job is, what sort of accommodations and assistance will be necessary for the person to be successful there? What will the person need to learn to do? What kind of help will the person's employer, supervisor, and co-worker need in order to support the person's success on the job?

In some places it is easier to do this than it is in other places. Some service systems have been learning how to support people with substantial disabilities in real jobs for more than twenty years. Not everyone with a substantial disability in these communities works in a real job, but people in these places have good reasons to accept the liberating belief that people can work, given the opportunity and the support they need. In other places, the service system has not even started to learn how to assist people with substantial disabilities to work. These places wait for pioneers who will challenge what "everybody knows."

Turning Limiting Beliefs Into Positive Possibilities

Start with a limiting belief and map out a negative belief-opportunities- experiences cycle.

Pick one from your own experience or from the table on page 32.

Belief

Experiences

Opportunities

Circle of Discouragement & Confinement

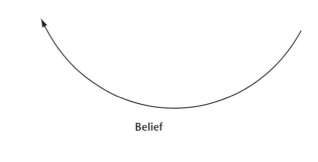

Belief

Turn the limiting belief into a positive possibility and map out a positive belief-opportunity-experience cycle.

Experiences

Opportunities

Circle of Courage & Contribution

Practice Capacity Thinking

Deciding to practice capacity thinking is the most important thing anyone can do to keep from being captured by limiting beliefs about people with disabilities. Capacity thinking begins by discovering assets and gifts rather than beginning by identifying deficiencies and what is missing. It is the art of seeing the glass half full and acting to make the best of what you see.

The art of discovering…

…what people can contribute to community life

Capacity Thinking

…ways that people can make their contribution

The rule is: find ways to do more of what works

Capacity thinking sets a positive cycle in motion. A person who identifies something they can contribute and finds a way to make their contribution almost always discovers more ways to contribute.

Learning to practice capacity thinking is like learning to play a musical instrument or tuning an engine or making great pies. You have to practice and you have to look at the results and think about how to improve next time. You never get finished improving; there is always more to learn. The rule is: find ways to do more of what works.

Capacities show up when people look and listen for them. There is no way to discover capacities from a distance. You can't search for them on the internet, or find them in a directory, or read about them in a file. You have to spend time with people listening to what they care about and what works for them. You have to walk around, explore, and ask questions. The best questions focus on capacities –"Tell me about a time when you were at your very best. What abilities did you show?" and caring – "What matters to you enough to take action?" You have to imagine ways that people could benefit from making new uses of what's available.

Look for capacities in four places:

• The person

- Family, extended family, and friends
- Neighborhood and community
- The service system and its staff

It is very easy for capacities to get buried by deficiency thinking. Somehow, many of us find it easier to list problems and complain about what we don't have and can't do. Deficiency lists can quickly get so long that we get discouraged from taking any positive action, and so, people's gifts go unnoticed and unreceived.

Deficiency thinking can be especially powerful in the lives of people with disabilities.

> This job demands self-exploration. I had negative attitudes about disability that I didn't even know were there. Maybe I still have some, but fewer than before I really got to know people.
>
> –Direct Support Worker

- People's capacities can be hard to see without taking a new and deeper look. This is especially true for people who have grown up receiving services that are based on low expectations of what they can do, learn, and become.

- Some people are cut off completely from their families, and lack allies who remember their life stories and stand up for them. Some people and families have never experienced an asset-sharing relationship with service providers and so they focus on avoiding threats rather than pursuing opportunities.

- In many places services for people with disabilities have been set up to provide places that group people with developmental disabilities together, supervise them, and try to keep them safe, healthy, busy, and happy. In services that operate this way, it takes extra work to act to create opportunities for people to bring their gifts to people in the community. It can be hard to find the time and flexibility to do this extra work.

> Deciding to practice capacity thinking is the most important thing anyone can do to keep from being captured by limiting beliefs

- Possibilities for community connections can be hidden by fear of prejudice against people with disabilities or by community characteristics that hide assets –poverty, remote or unsafe location, "everybody here just keeps to themself" lifestyles.

- It's easy to see disabilities as deficiencies that need formal services.

This last belief, that disability equals deficiency, is worth thinking about carefully. If we think that the people we support are deficient, then it will seem unrealistic, and maybe even cruel, to try to assist them to act as contributing citizens. They are broken in ways that only specially devoted or qualified people can cope with.

> The differences are really obvious. What I have learned is that you can't understand the differences until you understand the ways we are similar. Until you recognize how much you are like the person you are helping, your help will be sort of a put down.
>
> – Direct Support Worker

Unless we are careful

Difference

is seen and treated as

Deficiency

& the person is

Devalued

which leads to

Being Excluded & Controlled By Others

In one way it seems obvious: a person gets labeled disabled because they can not do something that normal people of their age can do –roll over, crawl, use words, follow three step directions, read– or because they do something that normal people of their age find weird or frightening or dangerous – repeat the same words over and over, respond to voices that others don't hear, repeatedly hit their head against something hard. This observation says what anyone can see: that disability means difference. It is a another step to say that these kinds of differences equal deficiencies, and a big step beyond that to believe that difference means being of less value as a person. This second step, the one that turns difference into deficiency, gets hidden under the word "normal".

Leaders with disabilities strongly challenge this way of understanding "normal" because it sets people up to think about the world as divided into "us", the normal, and "them", the deficient. The belief that the differences that come with impairments equal deficiencies is dangerous because it makes an excuse for setting some people aside as lesser beings.

The United States Congress agrees that society needs to reconsider the idea that disabled means different and devalued:

> *Congress finds that… disability is a natural part of the human experience that does not diminish the right of individuals with developmental disabilities to live independently, to exert control and choice over their own lives, and to fully participate in and contribute to their communities through full integration and inclusion in the economic, political, social, cultural, and educational mainstream of United States society…*
> *– Developmental Disabilities Assistance and Bill of Rights Act of 2000*

The first step in moving this Congressional finding from words on paper into the way people with developmental disabilities live their lives is taking down the walls that separate "us" from "them". Taking down these walls begins with noticing and naming them. Some walls are as physical as the fence around a residential facility or the special bus that takes people far from their neighborhood to a building that gathers many people with disabilities in one place. Some walls are in the written and unwritten rules that restrict people's opportunities. Some walls are in the ways we talk and think. The worksheet on the next page gives you a chance to reflect on the ways we can build walls out of words.

The Language of Us and Them
Mayer Shevin

We like things.

> They fixate on objects.

We try to make friends.

> They display attention-seeking behaviors.

We take a break.

> They display off-task behavior.

We stand up for ourselves.

> They are non-compliant.

We have hobbies.

> They self-stim.

We choose our friends wisely.

> They display poor peer socialization.

We persevere.

> They perseverate.

We love people.

> They have dependencies on people.

We go for walks.

> They run away.

We insist.

> They tantrum.

We change our minds.

> They are disoriented and have short attention spans.

We are talented.

> They have splinter skills.

We are human.

> They are...?

© 1987 Mayer Shevin

Noticing How Words Build Walls

Use this space to list some of reasons that staff would use "The Language of Us and Them" and some of the results of using it.

Reasons	Results

Mayer says: This is a poem that says in one page most of what I know about the power of words to oppress people. It was written in great anger during a series of three meetings at a state institution in which twenty people were arguing over whether a 60-year-old man, a life-long resident of the institution nearing the end of his life, would be allowed to own a harmonica. All of the negative statements in this poem were said about that man during the course of those meetings.

Read the story of Barney's Harmonica at www.shevin.org/

Think about it: Mayer wrote this poem in 1987. Do you still hear language like this today? Do you hear a new "Language of Us and Them" that uses different words to separate people with developmental disabilities from staff?

41

People with disabilities help to heal the fear of disability by personal connections to others who have not had the chance to know people with disabilities before.

One reason we build the walls of "US" and "THEM" is fear of difference. No one has come up with a complete explanation for this fear. Maybe we fear our own weakness, imperfection, and mortality and the way we see people with disabilities reminds us of these facts of life. Maybe we fear and resent dependence and the way we see people with disabilities makes us think of them as a threat to our sense of independence. Maybe we are looking for a group to blame for our social problems.

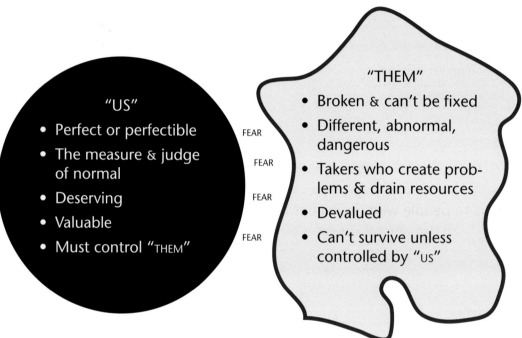

"US"
- Perfect or perfectible
- The measure & judge of normal
- Deserving
- Valuable
- Must control "THEM"

FEAR
FEAR
FEAR
FEAR

"THEM"
- Broken & can't be fixed
- Different, abnormal, dangerous
- Takers who create problems & drain resources
- Devalued
- Can't survive unless controlled by "US"

Whatever the reasons for the fear, one thing is true. Many, many people with disabilities have helped to heal this fear by becoming personally connected to others who have not previously had a chance to know people with disabilities. That's why it is so important to assist people to act as contributing citizens. It not only makes life better for individual people, it also helps our society overcome fear of disability. Unless fear and exclusion are overcome, we stay caught in an irrational pattern: fear feeds the social exclusion of people with disabilities, which means that people with disabilities are not real to their fellow citizens, which leads us to spend more and more on keeping up the walls that separate people from each other. This simply wastes people's lives.

Direct support workers can step outside of this irrational pattern by assisting people with developmental disabilities to act as contributing citizens.

What Do You Believe?

	Agree	Not Sure	Disgree
Disability is a natural human experience.			
People with disabilities have the same rights and responsibilities as every other citizen.			
People with disabilities are far more like people without disabilities than they are different from them.			
All people have something important to contribute to other people: gifts and talents that can make a positive difference.			
Negative beliefs and poor attitudes are much bigger barriers to people with disabilities making a contribution than their impairments are.			
Communities and the people in them have a great capacity to welcome and include people with disabilities.			
People with disabilities are ready to be included in their communities right now.			
Communities have places that are ready to include people with disabilities right now.			
The way services are set up and delivered can be a major barrier to people being included.			
All people can learn and grow, regardless of disability labels.			
Helping people discover, develop, and use their gifts and talents is the most important thing that service workers can do.			

Find Direction

It's easy for people with developmental disabilities to get trapped in low expectations and have to settle for second class citizenship. It helps to have a way to think about what the good things in life are for any person. One way to do that is to identify experiences that most people value and use conversations about these experiences to guide action. Valued experiences are some of the benefits that come to any person who is acting as a contributing citizen. They matter to people with developmental disabilities as much as they matter to anyone else, but they are not limited to people with disabilities. These experiences are as important to workers as they are to the people they assist.

Looking for ways that workers can create conditions that protect or promote these experiences increases the meaning that you find in direct support work.

Together, these five valued experiences define a star that people can steer by as they take stock, set goals, and deal with obstacles and problems along the way to a good future.

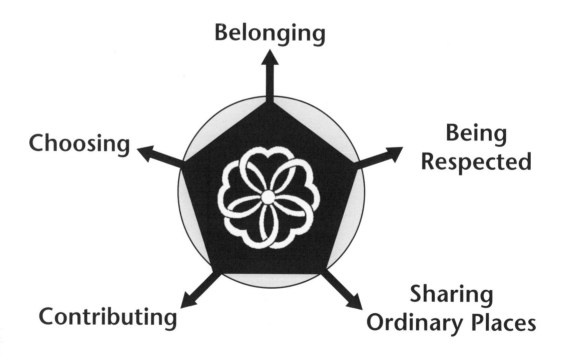

Enable valued experiences

Everyone's world grows richer and more interesting when people have more opportunities for these valued experiences.

- **Belonging**: Being a member of a group or an association or a congregation; being a friend; being a family member; being a partner. Having a variety of relationships and memberships including associations with both people with developmental disabilities and people without developmental disabilities, both paid staff or volunteers and other citizens.

- **Being respected**: Being seen and treated with dignity; being seen and treated as a whole person; being seen and treated in ways that honor the best in your culture; being seen and treated as a person with rights; being seen and treated in ways that fit your age.

- **Sharing ordinary places**: Making the same uses of community settings as any other citizen does, at the same times and for the same purposes as other citizens do: living, working, learning and playing confidently in ordinary places.

- **Contributing**: Making a positive difference to other people, to community groups, and to the community at large by discovering, developing, and giving individual gifts and using personal capacities. There are gifts of being and gifts of doing: contributions can include interested presence as well as capable performance; in some situations simply being present and involved makes a real difference. Contributions can be freely given or earn pay.

- **Choosing**: Having the freedom and support and assistance to make the same sorts of choices as other people of your age and to learn to make wiser choices over time. As an adult, making big decisions (such as where and with whom to live and work) and smaller decisions (like what to eat and when to go to bed). At any age, being encouraged to use and strengthen your voice (in whatever way works for you to communicate), to clarify what really matters to you, to make thoughtful decisions, and to learn from experience.

If you have a legal guardian, your guardian does not make any decisions for you that you can make for yourself, commits to

It's hard being the responsible person: being accountable to the people you support and to the organization for making sure that people get what they need. And doing that without falling into acting like people's boss or feeling really superior to them is pretty challenging.

–Direct Support Worker

knowing you personally and discovering your preferences, makes substitute decisions by standing in your shoes and looking at the situation from your point of view, seeks your ideas and opinions about substitute decisions as much as possible, informs themself about alternatives and possibilities, and respects your preferences and values.

Each person is different, so these five valued experiences are the starting place for a conversation, not a prescription that tells a person what they must do. We come from different cultures, ethnic identities, and family and personal histories. We have different temperaments: some of us like a lot of activity and others like it quieter; some of us seek out other people and others enjoy alone time; some of us like to take things slowly and others prefer a fast pace; some of us know emotionally and others stop and think. Each of us is a unique constellation of capacities: ability to make music; ability to move in powerful, coordinated and graceful ways, ability to understand and respond to one's own and other's feelings and intentions; ability to see and use mathematical and logical patterns; ability to use spoken and written language and symbols; ability to understand and make mechanical things; and ability to relate knowingly to the natural world. Given the opportunity, we will spend time in different places if we come from a family who shares a love of the outdoors, likes action, and has a great sense of what is going on in nature than if we come from a family that loves big city life, prefers lots of social time indoors, and shares a gift for dance. What matters is understanding what the valued experiences mean at this time in each person's life. The only way to gain this understanding is to listen respectfully to what the person says in words and actions.

Many people notice that the list of valued experiences is incomplete. Some people would add a sixth point to the star and call it spirituality, other people's sixth point might be called health or creativity. Other people's stars might have seven, eight, or nine points. That's fine as long as each point on the star represents something deeply important to the people involved and it is the starting point for a conversation about what this means for the person and how we can work together to protect or increase the person's experience of this valuable quality.

Some people just can't see past the labels. They don't work to get to know and understand the real people in front of them because they think they know all they need to know when they see the schedule of tasks to do.

–Direct Support Worker

The valued experiences we have chosen have five things in common.

- They are not about disability but about what matters to most people, disabled or not. A person's impairments might affect the way they get these valued experiences, but it does not make them less important.

- Each person plays a part in creating the valued experiences and each person needs others to create the valued experiences. A valued experience is not a thing that can be bought by a consumer like a restaurant meal. People make valued experiences happen by the way they act together, like friends who create a wonderful potluck supper.

- The experiences are related to each other. Actions to promote one experience can strengthen the others. A person who uses more of a community's ordinary places usually has more options to choose among. A person who has a wider network of relationships and memberships usually has an easier time finding opportunities to make a contribution. A person with confidence that they have something worthwhile to give usually finds it easier to engage other people. Sometimes looking for more of one valued experience conflicts with or limits others. Some choices may be ruled out because of their effect on an important relationship. Pursuing a path to contribution channels a person's choices and relationships.

- The assistance a person gets makes a difference. History clearly shows that it is very easy for people with disabilities to miss out on these experiences. If the people who organize and offer the help the person needs to get through the day don't choose to work creatively on the problems involved in assisting people to have these experiences, the people with developmental disabilities who count on them have a good chance of being treated disrespectfully, being separated from ordinary people and places, lacking support to develop and give their gifts, having little control of their lives, and having restricted connections to other people.

- Promoting these experiences builds healthy communities. When people with disabilities seek more of these good things, they challenge prejudiced beliefs and practices that may be common among community members.

> You can get caught in a negative spiral: what you are doing with the people you support doesn't stimulate you, so you blame them for it by thinking they are too limited to do anything interesting with, that makes you bored and tired, people read that from you and draw away into their shells, that makes them less stimulating and more tiresome to spend time with. Imagine what it must be like for the people with disabilities to get through a shift with somebody like that.
>
> –Direct Support Worker

How Will An Idea For Making Things Better Increase Valued Experiences

Use this worksheet to evaluate ideas for improving assistance to a person. Come up with a short title for the idea and write it in the circle in the middle. Then, think about how implementing the idea will increase the chances that the person will have more of each valued experience. List the positive possibilities next to each valued experience.

Ways that doing this will increase belonging:

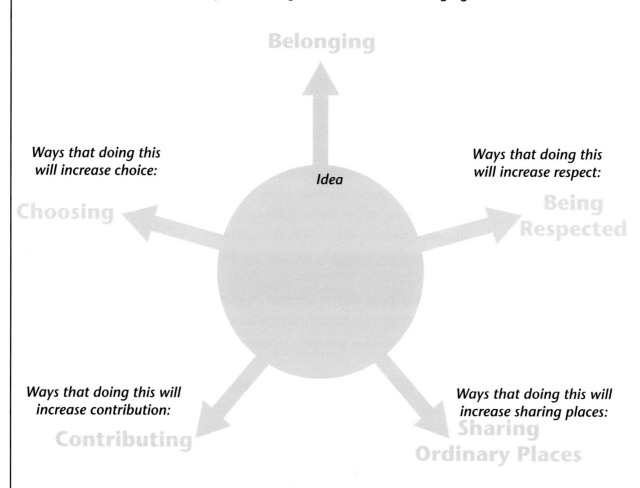

Belonging

Ways that doing this will increase choice:

Choosing

Idea

Ways that doing this will increase respect:

Being Respected

Ways that doing this will increase contribution:

Contributing

Ways that doing this will increase sharing places:

Sharing Ordinary Places

Build healthy communities

People with developmental disabilities and their allies sometimes have to overcome patterns shaped by generations of "us" and "them" thinking in order to get more of the valued experiences that make for a good life. Not letting these patterns of prejudice take control of a person's life builds a healthier, more just, and more resource rich community. In communities that are working to be healthier, more and more citizens invest in building up the capacities to promote valued experiences for everyone.

Citizens make ordinary places accessible and welcoming by finding creative ways to **adapt to and accommodate differences** that might otherwise keep people out. Differences in ability to move, differences in language, differences in sensing and processing information, and differences in learning can call for changes that adapt the physical environment or the social rules in order to make room for new people. Differences in appearance and past experience may take mutual tolerance and willingness to find a way past stereotypes.

Citizens **see and support capacities**. This means looking first at what people can do and what opportunities are available to allow the person to contribute rather than getting stuck on what people can't do or what resources are missing.

Citizens look for **fair and creative ways to resolve conflicts**. When people whose voices have been left out of decision making begin to be heard, new problems come up about who has power and how they use it. A healthy community finds ways to figure out how people can redistribute power and work together so that each can get more of what matters most to them. Conflicts are not covered up and people do not have to resort to violence or withdrawal to deal with them.

Citizens **create inclusive stories** by living with each other in a way that respects and celebrates the benefits of difference. Stereotypes and mistaken beliefs reinforce exclusion. Shared experiences break down stereotypes and build stronger communities.

Citiens **promote interdependence**. Independence isn't a matter of doing things alone, it's a matter of having what you need to live your life in a way that makes sense to you and the people who care

Everyone needs other people who know them and value their contribution.

The better I get to know a person, the less I see disability.

–Direct Support Worker

49

Lessons In Welcome

Think about a time that you learned something important about welcoming a stranger –someone who seemed very different, at least at first. This might be a person with a disability, but it need not be. Use this space to write about what happened and what you learned about creating welcome. Were there any fears in the situation; if there were, what worked to deal with them? Were there awkward or uncomfortable moments: if there were, what worked to deal with them? What were the good things and what were the hard things about bringing a stranger in from the outside?

What happened?

What I learned from this about making people with differences welcome.

-

-

-

deeply for you. A big part of what everyone needs is other people who know them and value their contribution. The more people know that they can trust each other and count on each other for help, the more strength they have to make the most of opportunities and to cope with hard times. A whole community is weaker when people hide from each other and stay disconnected. People have more reasons to be afraid and more reasons to hide their gifts. People are healthier and more prosperous when they have a variety of ties and connections to others. In a strong community, citizens support a wide variety of groups and associations and value people who build bridges among different groups. They act everyday on the belief that "together we are better."

> I used to think there was dependence (not so good) and independence (good). I have figured out that interdependence makes a much better way to understand what I do. What I do is needed, but that need is met in an interdependent relationship .
>
> – Direct Support Worker

These investments in building healthy community are risky. Changing patterns of using power to keep some people out and under control can be very hard, especially when those who have been excluded are angry at being disrespected, excluded and kept down or when people are discouraged because they believe that those with power are too strong to have to make any changes. There may be good reasons to be angry or discouraged about how many obstacles stand between people with disabilities and a fair chance to participate in ordinary life. But there are also chances for people with developmental disabilities and their allies to successfully challenge their community to be more just and more inclusive. As you will see in the stories later in this book, these challenges are not usually about loudly confronting people. They are usually about persistent and thoughtful invitations to make room for someone who can make a positive contribution.

Not letting prejudice take control of a person's life builds a healthier, more just, and more resource rich community.

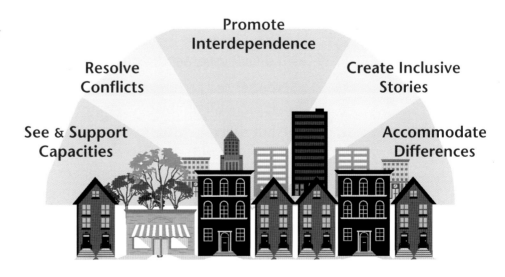

Promote Interdependence

Resolve Conflicts

Create Inclusive Stories

See & Support Capacities

Accommodate Differences

Build bridges not walls

Organizations that serve people with developmental disabilities can make it easier or harder for the people they support to act as contributing citizens and have valued experiences.

In the past, the mission of most services was to contain and control people, either to protect them from the threats of unaccepting communities or to protect communities from the demands and dangers they were thought to cause. Services built special and separate buildings that gathered together large numbers of people with similar labels. Staff controlled the details of people's everyday life and often believed that they were doing so for people's own good. Staff focused their attention on what people could not do and generally had low expectations for what people could learn. In some places staff treated people nicely, although they often treated people in paternalistic ways rather than recognizing them as equals. In other places staff were domineering and demanded obedience, punishing or neglecting people who did not follow staff directions. These practices created a sort of a separate world. People with disabilities made their friendships within the walls of their programs, mostly among others with labels like their own. If they had a contributing role, it was within the small world created by their special program. If they were present to community life it was usually as one of a group of people with developmental disabilities. They did what staff told them to do. They were segregated from community life. These services made barriers: to get the assistance necessary to live their lives, people with developmental disabilities had to stay within program walls.

> I've gained a lot of respect for what people have endured. Rejection. Prejudice. Discrimination. People coming and going in their life. Even abuse. And mostly they come through it willing to keep on with life, willing to reach out and get to know me.
>
> –Direct Support Worker

Some service organizations still gather groups of people with developmental disabilities together and keep them under staff control. But more and more organizations have a different mission: to assist people with developmental disabilities to be contributing citizens and to have valued experiences. Staff work creatively to offer the assistance that people want and need; people are not made to fit in to existing services. The service organization acts like a bridge to community life, not as a barrier.

When a service organization supports people to have valued experiences, it learns with the people it assists and their allies how to create five accomplishments by coming up with better and more reliable ways to answer five questions.

How do we enhance people's reputation? An effective service organization keeps learning how to **encourage valued social roles**. People give respect to those who play a recognizable and valued part in everyday life. Acting as a good neighbor, being a co-worker, singing in the chorus of the little theatre musical, being a loyal brother or sister, being a good uncle or aunt, collecting money for an important cause, acting as spokesperson for a community's interests, working on the clean-up committee for a local festival, volunteering to shop for elders, playing first base on the workplace softball team –all of these roles draw respect. Service workers make an important contribution when they assist people to identify and take up social roles that match their interests and negotiate or offer the accommodations and assistance people need to play their role. In all of their work they model respect for the person in the way they treat the person and the way they communicate with and about the person. They see the person as a valued citizen with a contribution to make.

> Advocacy is an important part of my job. Society needs exposure to the people I support. They have important benefits to offer people who don't know them yet – and I get to help people meet and understand each other.
>
> – Direct Support Worker

How do we increase peoples' presence in the life of their communities? An effective service organization keeps learning how to promote **community presence**. Every community offers hundreds of different settings: places to work, places to learn, places to shop, places for entertainment, places to enjoy nature, places to worship; places to exercise, places to hang out and gossip, and places for political discussion and action. Direct service workers can assist people to make confident use of a place by discovering what, if anything, people need to know in order to make the most of it. For some people this might mean figuring out how to take their turn or how to pay for what they want, For others it might mean helping other people notice how to use a person's communication device to have a conversation.

How do we assist people to develop their capacities? An effective service organization keeps learning how to **develop capacities**.

Each person is a unique constellation of gifts, skills, and abilities. People have different capacities in the use of their minds, their hands, their feelings, and their bodies. Capacities shape the ways people keep their homes, the kinds of work people find satisfying, and the kinds of learning and leisure activities they enjoy. Capacities flourish when they are exercised and wither when they are not used. Many capacities grow with good instruction or coaching. Direct support workers can see and acknowledge each person's capacities, assist people to connect with opportunities to use their capacities, and find ways to help people strengthen them.

In a way, we are like a guest in people's homes. They need us to be there, but that doesn't give us the right to take over and do everything our way. Sometimes we have to negotiate, and some things are set by rules or schedules, but it works best for everybody when we make an effort to do things that people want in the way people want to do them.

– Direct Support Worker

How can we help people have more choice and control in their lives? An effective service organization keeps learning how to **support autonomy**. People with disabilities have rights and responsibilities to make choices about how they want to live and how they want to be assisted. Direct support workers can help people to think through choices, gather and sort information and advice, develop a sense that they can decide and do what seems good to them, recruit people to support and encourage them, and learn from the results of their choices.

How can we assist people to make and maintain friendships and memberships? An effective service organization keeps learning how to actively support **community participation**. Being present in community places is a start, but playing a valued role in the community calls for active participation. If necessary, direct support workers can assist people with the practical tasks involved in keeping up a friendship or a membership: arranging rides, being ready on time, sending birthday cards, making calls, baking cookies for the bake sale. They can help the person let others know how to understand them or provide them with what they need to be successful.

Conflicts between a commitment to accomplishments and...

...what a person says that they want

...the way a program is set up

...the climate at work

Staff in an organization committed to these accomplishments have to deal with three kinds of conflicts. There can be a conflict between what a person they support wants and their commitment, there can be a conflict between the way a program is set up and their commitment, and there can be a conflict between the climate at work and their commitment.

Our commitment vs what the person wants now. Sometimes people are out of touch with their gifts and lack confidence that they can make a contribution that others will value. Sometimes people have been so wounded by rejection that they have no desire to reach out to connect with others. Sometimes people feel like it's better to depend on someone else to make their choices for them. Sometimes people seem to treat themselves disrespectfully and even seem to invite others to disrespect them. In other words, sometimes people don't value the valued experiences. This creates a conflict between what the person wants and the organization's values. It would be wrong to try to force a person to do what the organization thinks is right; it would be a failure if a person missed out on the good things that come from participating as a contributing citizen.

There is no easy way out of this conflict, but respect comes first and forms the foundation for the kind of relationship that may, over time, encourage the person to reach for more of the good things in life. A respectful view allows us to see the way the person's capacities and interests show up in their life and to invite people to try something new that will expand their experiences. This kind of respect sends two messages: "I value you as you are." *and* "I see you as capable of making an even bigger contribution to even more people and I want to assist you to do it."

Our commitment vs the way our services are designed. Every organization has some things about it that make it easier to learn to create the accomplishments with the people they support and some things that make it harder to learn how to create them. Some service programs were set up to serve a different mission than the promotion of choice, contribution, and community participation in valued roles. Programs that gather people together and assign staff to buildings or groups have more conflicts to deal with than programs that have the flexibility to provide individualized assistance, based on the choices of a person and their allies.

Our commitment vs the climate at work. Making the accomplishments real often calls for learning to do new things in new ways. A work climate that supports strong relationships, encourages positive action. and drives out fear and negativity makes learning easier.

Respect sends two messages: "I value you as you are." and "I see you as capable of making an even bigger contribution to even more people and I want to assist you to do it."

For good ideas on improving the climate at work, download David Pitonyak, *Toolbox for Change: Reclaiming Purpose, Joy, and Commitment in the Helping Profession*. Free from www.dimagine.com

How do we enhance people's reputation?

How do we increase peoples' presence in the life of their communities?

How do we assist people to develop their capacities?

How can we help people have more choice and control in their lives?

How can we assist people to make and maintain friendships and memberships?

Almost everyone has to live with the tension between what they want to accomplish and the way their organization currently functions. Let this tension motivate real change. It's easy to run away from this tension between accomplishment and current reality by seeing yourself as a powerless. If you think, "no one will let me do what I believe would make life better for the person I assist", think again and make the choice to make a difference.

If you accept responsibility for working with others to make your organization even more effective than it is now, you will find ways to clearly imagine the kind of lives you want to assist people to live, honestly describe your current ability to help this to happen, and look for ways to increase the organization's capacity. (Use the worksheets on the next two pages to describe the current reality in your workplace.) These moves can be small as long as they are based on real partnership between staff and a person with a developmental disability and the person's allies.

When staff commit themselves to learning how to work with the people they assist to create these accomplishments, the people who count on them for help have a real chance for a good life.

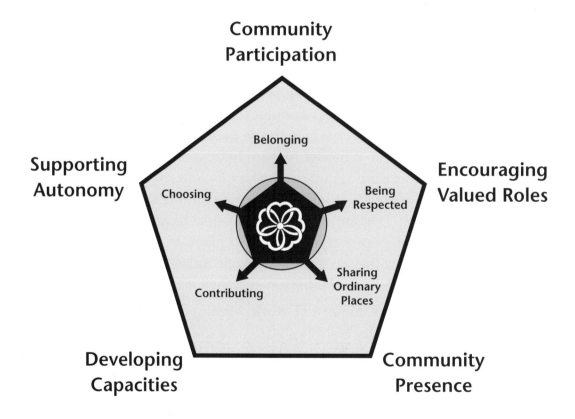

At the present time…	True (more room to learn)	False (less room to learn)
The way our program is set up…		
…People choose where and with whom they live.		
…People live in their own homes, not in group homes or apartments owned or leased by a service agency.		
…People choose what they do during the day.		
…Most people who want a job in an ordinary community workplace have the assistance they need to succeed at work.		
…We plan with people in a way that lets us individualize assistance to support what is important to the person.		
…People set goals for themselves that really stretch us		
…People (or their allies) direct an individual budget to select and customise the assistance they get.		
The work climate		
…As long as staff are not abusive or neglectful, there is little fear connected with making mistakes because we learn from them.		
…Our organization has a real interest in staff learning and growing.		
…We have an effective way to solve problems and make decisions.		
…Direct support staff are actively involved in decision making.		
…Paperwork does NOT take attention away from people.		
…Supervisors and managers treat staff with respect.		
…Staff treat one another and the people they assist with respect.		
…We take action to deal with staff who don't do their jobs.		
…People are proud to work here.		

Forces For and Against Making Your Organization Even Better

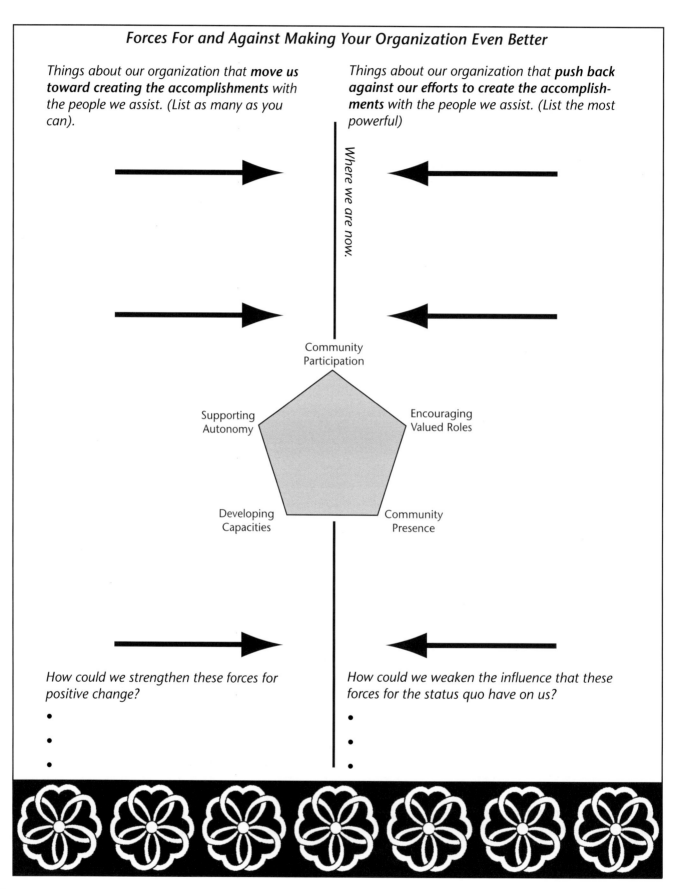

Things about our organization that **move us toward creating the accomplishments** with the people we assist. (List as many as you can).

Things about our organization that **push back against our efforts to create the accomplishments** with the people we assist. (List the most powerful)

Where we are now.

Community Participation

Supporting Autonomy

Encouraging Valued Roles

Developing Capacities

Community Presence

How could we strengthen these forces for positive change?

-
-
-

How could we weaken the influence that these forces for the status quo have on us?

-
-
-

Partnership for Excellence: A New Way of Organizing

Bruce Blaney

A new vision of direct support professionals (DSP's) and their roles emerged in the early 1990's to challenge the medical institutional model. The traditional roles of the DSP as sitter, attendant and skills trainer had grown out of the view of people with disabilities as both deficient and incompetent. The person-centered values base had at its core the experience of people with disabilities as fully human—as us not them.

The view of people with disabilities as people first engendered the role of the DSP as "maker of a difference" or "friend with a purpose" on the journey to lives at least as good as respected citizens.

What has become increasingly clear over the past decade is that the quality of the relationship between the DSP and the person supported is the foundation for providing quality support and achieving person-centered outcomes, especially for people with substantial support needs. Person-centered approaches are rooted in as deep a knowledge of the person as is attainable. The DSP is the person within any agency context who knows the person best, and in relationship with the person supported, comprises the foundation for creating relevant and effective supports.

Since 1997, Associates for Community Entry (ACE) has worked with more than 30 provider agencies (residential, vocational and support coordination) throughout Louisiana with a focus on creating person-centered organizations. The Partnership for Excellence project has integrated best practices in developmental disabilities and organizational development to create a person-centered organizational model as a network of direct support-led, person-centered teams.

Person-Centered Teams: Organizing for Real Life

Person-centered teams are the structural foundation of the person-centered organization. The teams comprise two to six direct support professionals, a mid-level professional and the focus person whom they support. A mid-level professional, who supports several teams, facilitates both a person-centered plan and periodic reviews of the plan. The team is empowered both by authority and resources to develop and implement the plan.

Person-centered teams are effective for three reasons:

1)The team, coupled with the person-centered planning process, builds on and amplifies the inspiring force of **identification**. At the core and origin of the medical institutional model is the failure to identify with people with disabilities—to experience people as essentially different from "us" or as Martin Luther King said, to "thingify" people. The central role of the person-centered facilitator is to support team members in identifying with the focus person –to experience on a deep level that "they" are "us." DSP's, in the absence of opportunities to identify, will lack the conviction essential to supporting people in lives like "ours" and will continue to support lives for "them"–including control, congregation and personal isolation.

Identification is able to shatter stereotypes and inspire team members to take action that will make a difference. The team approach amplifies and intensifies the impact of identification on team members and the focus person.

2) Person-centered values are about supporting real life, with a focus on roles and relationships. People, who have been excluded from real life, need opportunities to learn how to be "us"—to learn how to get a job, be a lover, a spouse, a homemaker, a friend, a neighbor, a church member. The most important contribution DSP's make to a person with a disability is to lend their **life experience**. DSP's have Ph.D's in life experience, which is virtually never tapped by the medical-institutional model's focus on health, safety and skills. When the focus is on real life, DSP's are able to exercise leadership and be remarkably creative.

The use of a team approach connects the focus person to a range of life experiences, a situation which amplifies and intensifies the learning context for the person with a disability.

3) The person-centered team supports the focus person in being able to identify with team members. Just as people without disabilities have stereotypes of people with disabilities, people with disabilities have powerful stereo-

types of people without disabilities. In the film, I am Sam, Sean Penn's character Sam, a young parent with an intellectual disability, at one point cries out to his lawyer in utter despair and terror that the court will take away his daughter:

You were born perfect and I was born like this. People like you don't know what it's like to try and try and never get what you want!

His stereotype of people without disabilities is immobilizing him, because only "perfect" people can act effectively. Sam's lawyer Rita, played by Michelle Pfeiffer, exclaims:

People like me feel lost and little and ugly and dispensable. People like me have husbands who are chasing someone far more perfect than me. People like me have sons who hate them. Every morning I wake up and feel I've failed. I'll never be enough!

Sam holds her and says, *You're much more than enough. Rita, you're much more than enough.*

A person-centered team is about such deep and mutual relationships among "friends with a purpose." As a network of interdependent relationships, the team supports staff and the focus person to shatter immobilizing and harmful stereotypes. The team and the focus person are engaged in a real life journey in which everyone's gifts and limitations are recognized.

The team approach supports the focus person in experiencing identification with several team members, which amplifies and intensifies the experience that we are all "us" and therefore all able to live lives of meaning, contribution and imperfection.

This combination of mutual identification, shared life experience,

collaboration and person-centered values creates an almost unstoppable force for changes that matter in the lives of people with disabilities.

The Person-Centered Organization: Shared Authority and New Roles

In the person-centered organization, authority and accountability are dispersed throughout the network of person-centered teams, in contrast to the traditional hierarchy, where position or level defines, roles, authority and accountability. What identifies the person in a person-centered organization is his or her role in relationship to the person supported. The issue is not position or title but what authority, information, resources and accountability does this team or team member require in order to support life changes that matter.

One of the deepest role changes, as described above, is that of the DSP—who becomes an empowered planner, actor, maker of a difference and leader within a person-centered team.

The dispersal of authority and accountability for life planning and plan implementation also necessitates deep role change for staff described as mid-level professionals. The mid-level professional within the traditional bureaucratic organization writes plans of care, assigns plan-generated tasks to DSP's and monitors DSP's in task completion. The role is bureaucratic, top-down supervision.

In the person-centered organization, the role of staff, to date defined by being in the middle of the hierarchy, is identified as both a capacity-building resource to the

team and an active partner in the team's work. That role is perhaps best summarized by his or her function as the person-centered facilitator, a role which supports the learning and leadership of DSP's and the person supported. He or she both supports the team and plays an active role in implementing the plan, especially by accessing needed resources or information, including training and technical assistance, and recommending agency policy changes.

Because he or she works with several person-centered teams, the new role might well be described as facilitator-coordinator, defined by his or her relationship to the focus person and the person-centered plan, not by level or position in a hierarchy.

A major challenge, in what amounts to a substantial redistribution of authority, is the role of the facilitator-coordinator in supporting the authority and accountability of the team. The team is the decision-making structure. If team members experience difficulty in making decisions or taking responsibility, the facilitator-coordinator seeks to affirm the authority and accountability of the team, at the same time refusing to retreat into the role of supervisor.

The executive director or executive team is key to initiating and sustaining the dispersal of authority and accountability, which is at the core of creating the organization as a network of person-centered, direct support-led teams. Executives develop policies and procedures to support the team structure including reward and opportunity structures, which incentivize teamwork over individual effort. Recognition focuses on team performance: It's no longer "employee of the quarter" but "team of the quarter", displayed in the reception area.

Executive leadership attends some team meetings, both to demonstrate support but also to learn. Person-centered teams are where the vision and mission of the organization is unfolding. Vision development is a global process: executives learn from teams and teams learn from executives through a circular dialogue which enriches and deepens the organizational vision.

The Voices and Roles of People with Disabilities in Person-Centered Organizations

Just as people do speak for themselves, leaders are needed to encourage others to listen. In a curious way, good listening is proactive self-advocacy. If people are heard and understood as a matter of course, they do not need to speak up in a deliberate sense. Being heard protects, for example, equal educational opportunity, universal access, freedom from stereotyping and the lives of people unwanted because they have disabilities.

– Michael Kendrick

What does it mean for the person with a disability to be at the center of the organization? As Kendrick emphasizes, effective self-advocacy hinges on effective listening. One key role of the person-centered organization is to create diverse formats where the voices of people with disabilities may be amplified and heard:

- Person-centered planning is the primary listening and learning forum: The agency from bottom to top is accountable for achieving the outcomes generated by listening to people with disabilities within these life planning sessions.
- People with disabilities participate on agency boards of directors and are supported in having a contributing role.
- People with disabilities are featured trainers within the agency's staff training program.
- People with disabilities participate in hiring staff and have the decisive voice in hiring and firing person-centered team members.
- The organization builds the leadership of people with disabilities in the broader community through support to participation in the self-advocacy movement or acting as statewide leaders by becoming, for example, trainers in the Partnership for Excellence.

The Alignment of Person-Centered Roles

The Organizational Framework
- The quality of the relationship between people with disabilities and direct support professionals is the foundation for quality support.
- The primary actors in planning are people with disabilities and direct support professionals functioning as empowered person-centered teams.
- People with disabilities are supported in leadership within person-centered teams, within the agency and throughout the state.
- Mid-level managers are resources, coaches and facilitators to the person-centered teams, who focus on shifting authority, resources, information and accountability to the teams.
- The role of the executive director or executive team is to create the context for developing a compelling vision of the organizational future—as a network of direct support-led, person-centered teams—rooted in feeling and thinking in terms of changes that matter in the lives of all the people supported.
- Service coordinators are in partnership with person-centered teams and act to access funding and other resources for team-developed, person-centered plans.

When staff roles are defined in relationship to the person and by person-centered values and organization, when, in short, there is person-centered alignment, powerful forces for deep change are set in motion. Such organizational changes and the commitment and creativity of innumerable actors are what it will take to close the gap between our values and the realities of life lived by people with disabilities.

(Answer the questions on the following page)

Reactions To the Idea of Person-Centered Teams

Do you agree that services should be delivered by the kind of person-centered teams described in this paper? Say why or why not.

Which ideas in this paper would you like to discuss with someone else?

Themes for Building Powerful Relationships

When we listened to effective direct support workers talk about what they do when they are at their best, we heard some ideas over and over again. We call these ideas **themes** because they come up in so many of the stories that flow from good direct support relationships. We think of each of them and all of them as challenges that call for life-long learning through careful planning and thoughtful action.

With the creative help of direct support workers, we have given each theme a name, created a symbol for it, and spelled out some of the actions that brings the theme alive in a direct support relationship. The symbol and name of each theme are on the next page, centered by the symbol that reminds us that this work engages our hearts, our minds, and our hands.

You will experience, through many walks with people, the incredible importance and value of relationships. You will discover that you are building a better and healthier world and community for the sake of humankind; that you are helping to take away the isolation in people's lives: that you are bringing equities that any citizen has a right to: that you are bringing care and compassion to people's lives: that you are building up the value in people that gives them the self-confidence and self-esteem to give to others rather than always taking; that you are bringing hope and light to people and their communities. And you will discover that without you the difference might never have been felt.

–Pat Beeman

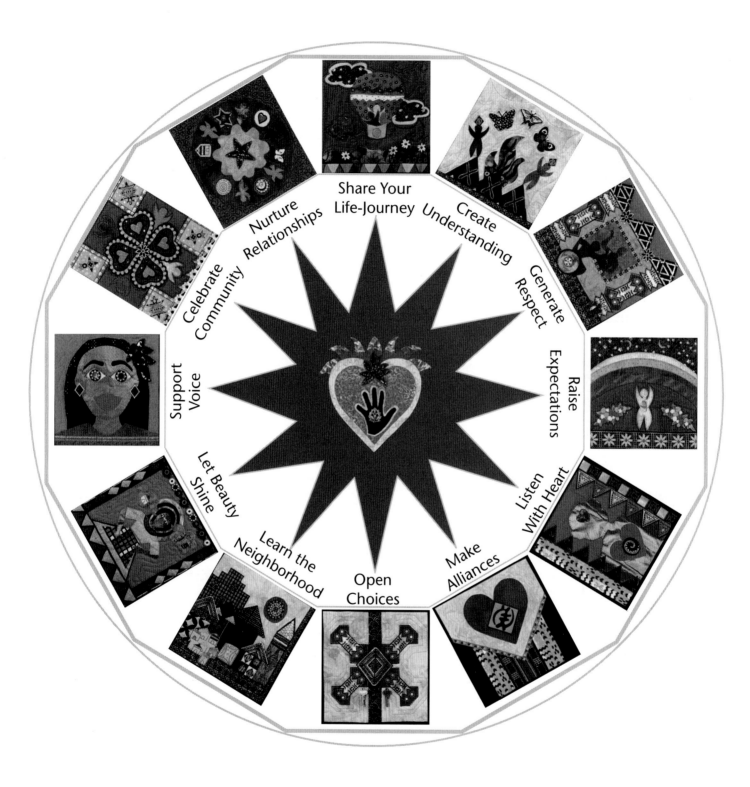

Share Your
Life-Journey

Create
Understanding

Nurture
Relationships

Generate
Respect

Celebrate
Community

Raise
Expectations

Support
Voice

Listen
With Heart

Let Beauty
Shine

Make
Alliances

Learn the
Neighborhood

Open
Choices

Share Your Life Journey

We see ourselves as companions, walking with people as they find their way in life.

Our differences make us resources to one another.

Create Understanding

We recognize the reality of prejudice and discrimination and work to overcome its bad effects.

We accept responsibility for creating understanding of each unique person.

Generate Respect

We honor the dignity of our common humanity.

We engage people with confidence, care and civility.

We follow through on our agreements.

Raise Expectations

We search out knowledge that will increase our idea of what is possible.

We encourage one another to pursue our dreams.

Listen With Heart

We find ways to see with the eye of our hearts.

We practice clearing away the fear, anger, and hopelessness that block our ability to understand.

We recognize that we can never know all there is to know about a person.

Build Alliances

We invest in others who can make a positive difference. Taking and encouraging positive action is the sign of an alliance.

We are honest in looking for creative ways to deal with conflicts.

Open Choices

We look for ways to increase opportunities.

We follow people's lead as much as possible.

We assist people to learn from their choices.

Learn the Neighborhood

We explore from the point of view of the person's (potential) interests.

We become regulars in local places.

Let Beauty Shine

We recognize each person's beauty.

We identify and encourage what lets that beauty shine through.

Support Voice

We find ways to assist communication and use what works in a disciplined way.

We encourage people to say what's important to them and to ask for what they really want. We negotiate.

We learn from honesty, especially when it threatens or angers us.

Celebrate Community

We get involved and encourage others to get involved in what's happening in community life.

We support local businesses and associations.

We find ways to help out those people who work hopefully for a stronger community.

Nurture Relationships

We offer, look for and appreciate hospitality.

We encourage next steps in friendship.

We actively assist people to stay in touch with important others.

We support reconciliation.

Everyday Heroes

The stories in the following twelve sections, and the images that illustrate the twelve themes, originated in the work of participants in the *Everyday Heroes* Project.

The *Everyday Heroes* project in New York State provides an example of ways that direct support professionals are deepening their relationships and making a difference in the lives of people with disabilities. These direct support workers are not only involved in creating community life for people, they also teach others about the wisdom and values expressed in their work. The twelve stories that follow illustrate the difference direct support staff make when they build community membership and belonging in company with people with disabilities. The people who created them together live and work in New York City and the Hudson River Valley.

Everyday Heroes began in New York City and at Westchester ARC in 2001 out of a desire to recognize the contributions of direct support workers, to support them to develop as leaders and teachers of other direct support workers, and to deepen their commitments and contributions to community inclusion through person-centered practice. Direct support leaders representing more than 60 agencies have participated in collaborative learning experiences throughout New York State, and helped develop training materials for other direct service staff.

The *Everyday Heroes* Quilt on the following page is a teaching tool generated from the insights of *Everyday Heroes* participants under the guidance of *Everyday Heroes* facilitators. The quilt is a sign of the collaboration, creativity and thoughtfulness of everyone involved in the *Everyday Heroes* Initiative. The hands around the border of the quilt represent each of the participants in the original Learning Institute, embellished with a symbol that distinguishes them, reflecting their individual mark on the world and their united efforts to support real lives for people.

A signature aspect of *Everyday Heroes* is that direct support staff use art, music, poetry, and storytelling to share their wisdom. Creative expression is reflected in the Everyday Heroes Workbook, Story Books, Video Tape, and yearly calendars through which participants in each project communicate good practice related to inclusion. The *Everyday Heroes* materials and teachings reflect the collective wisdom that emerges when direct support workers come together and inspire each other to have the courage to confront the discrimination that people face as they become valued community members. Heroes help each other gain strength when faced with limitation, and they support each other to see valor in actions that change lives.

The *Everyday Heroes* facilitators, Beth Mount, Denise Pensky, and Shelly Okure, have been involved in a continuous series of development activities that have encouraged the development of the project. Their work is supported by the New Yord State Office of Mental Retardation and Developmental Disabilities (OMRDD), particularly Kathleen Broderick, Associate Commissioner New York City Regional Office, and Dr. Allen Schwartz, OMRDD Director of Planning and Service Design, who have invested in the recognition of previously unsung support staff. The participants are sponsored by agencies that allocate time for direct support staff to meet, to take action, to address limitations, and celebrate accomplishments.

We are especially grateful to Westchester ARC, Ric Swierat, Executive Director, and Rosemarie Crisafi, Associate Director of Residential Services, who have made a significant commitment to developing direct support workers, and whose staff contributed several stories to this book.

The Everyday Heroes Quilt

A color poster of this quilt is available from www.capacityworks.com

Share Your Life Journey

We see ourselves as companions, walking with people as they find their way in life.

Our differences make us resources to one another.

This image symbolizes the joy of seeing past obvious differences in life to find common ground and mutual understanding that binds people together in their life journeys.

Share Life's Journey
Joey and Robert

One direct support leader has discovered the value of deep communication and friendship with people with disabilities. Joey attends a day program that focuses on assisting him to participate in his community. Before he met Robert, Joey's inability to speak was an apparent source of frustration for him. With Robert's support, the two have built a powerful relationship through which they have found an effective way to communicate with each other.

Joey loves listening to music, particularly the Beatles and Beach Boys, but he even enjoys listening to party songs for children. Robert shares Joey's love of music. He plays in a band and Joey will often select a CD that features Robert's songs. Immediately after boarding the van to embark on the days activities, Joey picks out a music CD, which becomes "the music of the day" and the two proceed to implement a daily schedule tailored to suit Joey's interests, preferences and needs. These activities may include mall walking, trips to the library, volunteering for Meals on Wheels, visits to Barnes and Nobles and shopping.

Why it works, according to Robert

- I start my day with Joey, and he is the only person I support.
- Joey and I have become friends.
- We like to spend time together.
- The day is for Joey and he knows it.
- Sometimes I think that Joey is the instructor and I am the student.
- We work to make each day interesting and different.
- We do things that are meaningful for Joey.
- Our relationship is based on mutual respect and common interests.

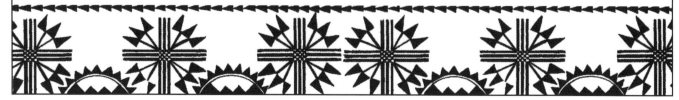

Robert chose this song as the background music for a presentation that tells the story of his life with Joey. The lyrics express the mutual appreciation between these two men, who each feel lifted up by knowing the other.

You Raise Me Up

Josh Groban

When I am down and, oh my soul, so weary

When troubles come and my heart burdened be

Then, I am still and wait here in the silence

Until you come and sit a while with me.

You raise me up, so I can stand on mountains

You raise me up, to walk on stormy seas

I am strong, when I am on your shoulders

You raise me up, to more than I can be.

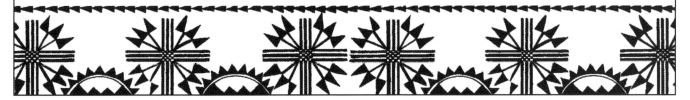

Bringing Who We Are to What We Do

Peter Leidy

Who are you?

Think about that for a minute. When have you been asked this before? Or should I say, have you been asked it before? It seems to be an uncommon question. Roger Daltrey sang it over and over in the Who's *Who Are You,* but he wasn't asking you or me.

When we meet someone we often start with "What's your name?" and proceed from there. What do you do, where are you from, have you read any good books lately – all of which may help us begin to learn who someone is.

Yet "Who are you?" is a wonderful question. I like the simplicity and the possibility in those three words.

Who are you?

How do you identify yourself? Imagine an assignment where you were asked to fill a page answering that one question. What would you say? Perhaps you would consider who and what is most important in your life, and how that connects to what's inside of you. What makes you feel most alive? Fortunately, these questions have no wrong answers, and there can even be many answers for each of us.

I've been curious lately about how this question relates to our work. Do we bring who we are to our jobs? In what ways? Does your job allow you to be who you are, or do you check your real self at the door and put on your job self? And what are the limits to being yourself at work? (Because surely there are some.) I wonder how we strike a balance on the job between being who we are outside of work and being "professional."

I heard someone in Georgia say that one of the reasons she loves her job is because she feels a sense of being "at home" in her organization. It is a good match for her, a work environment where she feels comfortable and where there is room to be herself. One example: she can wear open-toed shoes and blue toenail polish, unlike in the corporate world where she once was headed. For her, there is not the expectation that she "check" herself at the door.

Many support workers I've listened to say their work with people with disabilities allows them to live their values in their job. That who they are and what they believe to be important are reflected in the good work they are doing. Some might even experience author Frederick Buechner's definition of true vocation: "Where your deep gladness meets the world's deep need." And further, some say that what they bring – their true self, their gifts, their unique personality – is not only accepted, but even sought out by those around them at work.

But others have a different experience. Some direct support staff say that, despite believing in the importance of their work, there are few opportunities to share what they bring with them to their job. Sometimes this is because they are isolated in their work. No one is around much to ask the "Who are you?" or even "How's your family?" or "How's your dog?" Others find that there are plenty of people around, but the organizational culture does not invite or encourage more than "This is the job you are expected to do." I would bet that these are the people most apt to be keeping their eyes open for a different job.

I want to clarify that I am not talking about, say, a situation where service coordinator Brian, an accordion fanatic, is encouraged to play his accordion every day at work. Or where support worker Mary, a Rush Limbaugh fan, is permitted to listen to his program each day over the objections of the person she is supporting. There are limits to what we may bring to –or do at– work.

But, (and this is a big but) isn't it possible for Brian and Mary's employer to recognize their interests, talents, beliefs and see them as important to Brian and Mary? And maybe even find occasions from time to time where Brian can share his musical gift, and Mary could engage others in a political dialogue?

Can we respect, honor, even celebrate our differences? Can we get to know each other and appreciate the rich diversity in our organizations? Brian loves the accordion. Maybe I don't, but Brian does. Mary likes Rush Limbaugh. Maybe I don't, but I'm not Mary.

So we have Brian and Mary. And Jennifer who is a gifted seamstress. And Paul, who is gay, and Pam the baker, and Denise, whose great-great grandmother was a slave in South Carolina. They all have perspectives or talents or gifts that are not only important to who they are, but which may be important to others around them.

Then there's Carl, an artist. Not long after he began working for his supported living agency, his artistic gift started to become known. "Artist" would probably show up near the top of Carl's page-long answer to "Who are you?" Carl's agency values this part of who he is, and although hardly any of his job duties relate directly to art, the agency encourages Carl's artistic sense to come forth in his work, in many ways: offering his perspective with some people he supports in their art work, displaying pieces of his art at the office, lending his talents to agency projects.

Carl does not make his living as an artist; he makes it as a support worker. Still, he is an artist, and his agency understands that everybody wins when Carl weaves the artist in with the support worker. Everybody: Carl, the people he supports, his co-workers, and the organization.

Carl says he appreciates that he can be himself at work. In fact, he is grateful, because he knows it is a rare experience. He found a match, a "home" like the woman in Georgia. He is valued for the work he does and for who he is – for being the only Carl there. And this is a primary reason why he has remained in his job for seven years.

If Carl is right in thinking this is rare, can we "de-rarify" it? We're all too familiar with the workforce crisis. Pay is low. Status is low. Turnover is high. So it serves us well ("us" being people with disabilities, their families and friends, the service system and the community) to consider the reasons why some staff beat the odds and stay in their jobs longer than average.

I'm beginning to think that one reason is that, together with their employer, some support workers have figured out how to more fully integrate who they are with what they do. And I think we can learn from them.

What do YOU think?

In what ways do you bring who you are to your work?

What advantages and disadvantages are there to bringing who you are to what you do?

Who else do you want to discuss this paper with?

73

Live-With
Share Life's Journey

Live-Withs are calls to attention. Each *Live-With* invites you to focus for one week on one of the themes of person-centered direct support.

- Think about the theme at the beginning of each day.
- Notice things that happen that show you something important about the theme you are living with.
- Look for occasions to put the theme into action, maybe in a way that is new for you.
- Take a few minutes at the end of the day to review what you have discovered about the theme during the day.

Use the space on this page to summarize the main things you have learned by living with the theme for a week.

We are grateful to Michael Ray, teacher of creativity at the Stanford Business School, for the idea of *Live-Withs*.

Create Understanding

We recognize the reality of prejudice and discrimination and work to overcome its bad effects.

We accept responsibility for creating understanding of each unique person.

The butterflies in this image represent the transformative process of creating understanding and belonging from the flames of misunderstanding and rejection. The butterflies represent the capacity of the human spirit to rise above discrimination and form unity in the place of separation.

Create Understanding
Yolanda and Maritza

Maritza attends a day program in Spanish Harlem. The agency has been seeking ways for each person who attends the program to become involved as a community member in a way that fits each person's unique interests, connects them to others of similar cultural heritage, and builds on what is within walking distance from the program.

Maritza appears to like music, being close to familiar people, looking at colorful pictures, the breeze of a fan, and drinks of apple juice. She expresses her preferences via her eye gaze, relaxing her body, smiling, laughing, and clapping or rocking with excitement.

Maritza visits a local senior center, where she spends time with seniors, eats lunch, watches movies, and listens to the CD's she brings to share with others. Her connections have been remarkable; the seniors are delighted to share their mutual Spanish heritage with Maritza and she has made a friend, Esther, who spends a lot of time with her. and Esther calls Maritza her "adopted daughter."

Her direct support staff person, Yolanda, has facilitated Maritza's community connections. Yolanda initially contacted a senior center that did not seem open to Marizta's participation. They visited anyway, but after a few times, Yolanda concluded that they were just not welcome. Yolanda persevered in finding another senior center, and immediately appreciated the difference. Yolanda modeled to the others how best to relate to Maritza. Yolanda astute-

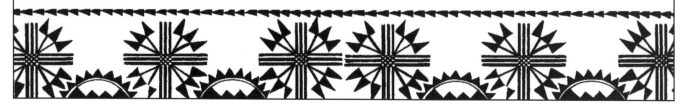

ly noticed Esther's interest in Maritza and supported the growth of their relationship. Success breeds success, and Maritza has become regularly involved in a number of community experiences including shopping trips to Hallmark, Path Mark, Bay Plaza Shopping Center, as well as using the post office, enjoying music at the movies and becoming a regular at El Rincon Latin Music Store, the New York Public Library, and Blockbuster video.

This is Yolanda's poem about her experience with Martiza and the people at the senior center.

Wonderful friends of Maritza, how could they be so kind,

Comparing Maritza's presence to " a pot of gold," as her potential does unfold.

As time went by, we found this Senior Center to be like a rainbow in Maritza's sky.

When I went in and asked questions about this place, to me it was amazing grace.

I met a lady with a big smile, who took the time to talk to us for awhile,

Before I even know what was at hand, Marita's life had a plan.

Maritza became a star that shined in the heart of a friend. Some people may not know how a heart can make a plan, but we know that Maritza understands.

There stood this lady with open hands, who welcomed Maritza in with lots of plans.

Now the window of life is filled with warm hearts and thoughts that everyone brought.

Like a Rose in Spanish Harlem, sunflowers and rain drops part, a rainbow emerged, and the pot of gold is the star in Ester's heart.

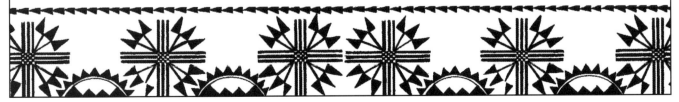

When Are You Going to Get a REAL Job?

Peter Leidy

I'm sitting here thinking about the work that goes into supporting people with disabilities to live and work in the community. In particular, the important work that direct service staff do.

Mostly, I am thinking about your and others' perceptions of your work. I wonder what you think about your job, and the kind of work you do. I wonder what *others* think about your job, particularly others who may be close to you but removed from the work you do –your family or friends. I wonder whether other people's opinion or knowledge of your work affects the way *you* feel about it.

So here I am, thinking and wondering. And drinking coffee.

This wondering comes from my own experiences of working directly with people with disabilities, and from conversations I've had with direct support staff that work part time and full time, those new to the work as well as veterans.

I wanted to write about this in hopes of sparking some conversations. I already know that some support workers relate to the ideas on these pages, but I'm curious how widespread the experience is. As you read this paper (which, you will notice, asks a lot of questions) think about yourself, and see what is or is not familiar.

Has anyone ever asked you the question that is the title of this paper, or raised the issue with a similar tone? Questions like this pop up from time to time in conversations some of us have with our families and friends. Sometimes the question is more subtle, like "Have you considered trying to move up in the company?" Or, "Do you still think about going back to school?" One person's father put it this way: "Why do you still have that job? You're wasting your education!" (That would be one of the *less* subtle examples.)

I think that most direct service workers believe their work is very important. I think that people who rely on them and agencies that employ them agree, even if it isn't always clearly demonstrated. I'd be curious to know what messages you as a support worker get from other people outside of your day to day work, for example, your mom, or your brother, or your friend from high school. Do you ever get messages from others that the job you have is undesirable, or unimportant, or perhaps worthwhile –but more suited for someone else?

Recently, I was talking with a man who has made direct support work his career. The foundation is the relationships he has with the men he supports. Of course, it is more than the relationships, because he is paid to support them. He has figured out how to do what he loves despite the obstacles he faces along the way: the money, status, bewilderment of some family and friends. It's tiring, he says, having to "make a case" for why he is doing what he is doing.

One thing he worries about is that a few (not most) direct support workers he knows don't seem to value the work that much. Maybe this is because they've chosen the wrong work to do, or because they think of it as a temporary or part time job that just helps pay the bills. He's concerned that their attitudes may rub off on the people in their lives, thus coloring the perception and status. Have you experienced this?

Or, consider how society views people with disabilities. Many people experience second-class citizenship because of having a disability. Sometimes, adults with disabilities are treated like children. Others feel invisible. To the extent that people with disabilities are not fully valued, what does this mean for those who support them? If your job is to assist someone who is not considered a whole person, or a person with much worth, how important can your job be?

And what *is* a real job, anyway? How does that get defined? Who decides? Again, we get messages –from the media, from family, and from other sources. Chances are real good that your high school guidance counselor did not have direct support listed in the array of possible careers you may want to consider. We have to decide what to accept, what to take with a grain of salt, what to reject. Some direct support workers have said (see if you agree) that these messages define a "real job" as having some of these characteristics:

- A real job is a profession, with a fancy title that begins with "Senior Vice President" or "Director of", or initials listed after your name (like R.N. or C.P.A.)

- A real job is full time, Monday through Friday
- A real job requires a certain education level
- A real job pays a salary, or a very respectable hourly wage, with good benefits

Most direct support workers I know –at least those who have stayed with the work and are committed to it– don't buy this prevailing sentiment. They believe their jobs ARE real jobs, even if by some measures, supporting someone with a disability does not fit society's definition. Yet even if you know that your job as a direct support worker is a real job, and an important one, the average person on the street may not have the same understanding.

Many support workers would argue that some of the above criteria for a "real job" are worth working toward, so that direct support becomes seen as a profession. I believe that many who do this work also understand the individual, unique nature of each job and relationship, and recognize the difficulty –if not danger– of trying to standardize jobs so they look more acceptable to others. In other words, they see the value and necessity of Susan's support worker being *Susan's* support worker—not just anybody's. Key to good community supports is keeping the support tailored to the individual, which includes designing direct support positions around what that person needs and wants (whether or not it results in jobs that look like what others might expect!)

As more and more people with disabilities rejoin their communities to live and work, the demand for personal assistants rises. Perhaps increased visibility and awareness of the contributions made by people with disabilities and those who support them, combined with increased advocacy efforts, will help change the perception and status of support workers. Then, some day, instead of direct support staff being asked, "When are you going to get a REAL job?" the question will be posed to people in other lines of work. Like telemarketers.

These are some of my thoughts and questions. What are yours?

In what ways does the fact that many people don't respect the job of providing assistance affect direct support workers' ability to understand people with developmental disabilities?

Who else do you want to discuss this paper with?

Live-With
Create Understanding

Live-Withs are calls to attention. Each *Live-With* invites you to focus for one week on one of the themes of person-centered direct support.

- Think about the theme at the beginning of each day.

- Notice things that happen that show you something important about the theme you are living with.

- Look for occasions to put the theme into action, maybe in a way that is new for you.

- Take a few minutes at the end of the day to review what you have discovered about the theme during the day.

Use the space on this page to summarize the main things you have learned by living with the theme for a week.

We are grateful to Michael Ray, teacher of creativity at the Stanford Business School, for the idea of *Live-Withs*.

80

Generate Respect

We honor the dignity of our common humanity.

We engage people with confidence, care and civility.

We follow through on our agreements.

This image represents reciprocity that is born from mutual respect and the opportunity to relate as equals. In African culture, the turtle represents the respect due to people who live long and endure much. In legends, the wise turtle always comes away victorious.

Generate Respect
Beverly and Ann

Beverly found attending a day program with 34 other adults too stimulating. This highly active program, with people coming and going constantly, and the prevailing sense of "organized chaos," left Beverly sad and frustrated at the end of the day. Despite all efforts to provide activities that met Beverly's interest, she was unhappy. Her unhappiness and frustration led to a hospitalization that lasted several months. After her medications were adjusted, she came back to the day program.

It was clear that she needed a different way to spend her day. The day program and its funder worked on a "life makeover" for Beverly. Just as the agency initiated its individualized support for Beverly, Ann returned from a leave of absence, and Beverly and Ann worked together to explore potential new interests for Beverly.

Beverly has found new interests, and has developed a penchant for all things historical. Through exploring the "I LOVE NEW YORK" website, she has discovered that Orange County is filled with fun things to do and see. She often strolls along the Newburgh waterfront in the morning before enjoying a light lunch in town. She visits the library to research new recipes to share with her housemates, or to plan her next visit to Washington's Headquarters for a quilt show or another similar event.

Ann has provided the support Beverly needs to select and participate in activities that are interesting and meaningful to her. Beverly has grown into a happier woman who has new knowledge and interests to share with others, and she enjoys sharing photographs of the spiritual, as well as physical journey she has traveled.

Lessons Learned:

• Think about what people face day to day.
• Make it a priority to help dreams come true.
• Consider dramatically different ideas for working with people.

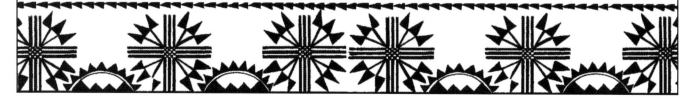

What'd I Say?

Peter Leidy

Think for a moment about how we talk about people we support. I've been listening to Ray Charles lately and just saw the movie *Ray*, so I couldn't help using a song of his as the title of this paper. But "What'd I say?" is more than a good song—it's a good question for us to ask ourselves. Our words are powerful. From what I've heard over many years in the service world, words spoken to or about people with disabilities are frequently limiting and not all that respectful. Usually, I think this happens without intending harm—I hope so anyway—but it happens.

There's a lot to this topic*; my hope is that this paper will start a discussion about the words we use, and the thoughts, beliefs, and feelings behind the words. We all know that direct support staff have important roles and close contact with the people they support; thus they—*you*—are key to the question of language.

There is no real list of language "do's and don'ts." This is not about what's politically correct – whatever that means these days. However, as we learn and evolve, attitudes change and the words we use change. Thankfully, words like "mongoloid" and "imbecile" and many others – words once widely considered acceptable descriptors of people with disabilities – have virtually disappeared from regular use. Hardly anyone would use them today in referring to someone with a disability. We are making progress—or are we?

Near the 2004 election, a radio host in Milwaukee used the word "wetbacks" while talking about illegal immigrants. There was a public outcry, because there is widespread agreement that you just don't do that. It's wrong. He was suspended, and after joking about apologizing, finally did apologize. A couple weeks later, a Madison radio host used derogatory terms about Condoleeza Rice and Colin Powell. A similar series of events followed. Andy Rooney, Howard Cosell, and numerous other public figures have found themselves in hot water over derogatory comments.

What I'm wondering is, how do we gauge what's acceptable and respectful in the language we use in support work and about adults with disabilities? Teen entertainer Lindsay Lohan recently received a letter from the Arc-USA, one of the largest disability organizations in the country, gently scolding her for her frequent use of the word "retarded" as a synonym for stupid, as in "That is so *retarded!*" This use of the word occurs regularly on TV, in movies, and in popular music. (I heard it most recently on the radio in the song *My Band* by D12 -- but some will be more offended by other lyrics in the unedited version of that song.)

But enough about famous people—back to us. Have you noticed that adults with disabilities are sometimes referred to as if they were children? I wonder if we agree that an adult is an adult, regardless of disability? One's life experience or intellectual development may be different or limited, but the person is an adult.

Yet I hear things like, "Mary is so spoiled." Whatever it is about Mary that would make her staff person say that, calling her spoiled is demeaning. What's underneath that? Doesn't Mary deserve better? Or, "I'm taking my girls to the zoo." Your girls? First, they're not yours, and second, they're not girls. A case manager (and speaking of language, think about those two words together...who is managing what?) says, "My people...."

Or this one: "Bill has the mental age of a one-year-old." Is that accurate and relevant? Does it matter? Who decided this, and how well do they know Bill? How does this opinion or medical diagnosis affect what people imagine as possible for Bill? I think the odds are pretty good that as this piece of "information" becomes part of the story told about Bill, following him around forever, Bill will be treated as a one-year-old his whole life.

I hear people use "high functioning" and "low functioning". I gotta say, I'm really tired of those terms. It seems to me that we *all* function differently, better in some ways than in others. Then there are words like profound, severe,

---

*There are a number of good resources on language and disabilities (see, for example, Kathie Snow's essay on people-first language at www.disabilityisnatural.com/peoplefirstlanguage.htm

moderate, and mild. I can accept that these classifications may serve a purpose, somewhere, to someone, but in twenty years I've never known them to matter much in real life. I think our words can create roadblocks to helping people make meaningful, real lives in the community. Would *you,* as a community member, be eager to get to know someone called "severe"?

"She's a Downs." I heard this not long ago when a staff person was talking about a woman with Down syndrome she supports. It was said in an effort to explain a certain behavior that the staff person believed was typical of people with Down syndrome. What do you think?

Here's a sentence taken from a newspaper story: "Wayne suffers from cerebral palsy." It was a story about a man who had been institutionalized for a long time who is now living in his own home. It was good news! He was beginning to live a full life and was apparently pretty happy about it. Nothing in his story was about suffering. But to the reporter, having cerebral palsy means Wayne must suffer. The reader has to wade through pity-evoking imagery to realize Wayne's life is good.

What the above examples have in common is that they tend to separate "them" from "us." They can

take some of a person's humanity away. They sell people short.

To me, it's worth thinking and talking about the language and style of speaking we use with and about people we support. Let's listen to each other and ourselves. Let's pay attention to how respectful we are being. I think we owe it to people we support.

As we go through our day, it might be worthwhile to occasionally stop and ask ourselves, "What'd I say?"

These are some of my thoughts. What are yours?

Do you agree or disagree with the idea that it is disrespectful to refer to people as "high functioning"? List three reasons to support your opinion.

-

-

-

Who would you like to discuss this paper with?

Live-With
Generate Respect

Live-Withs are calls to attention. Each *Live-With* invites you to focus for one week on one of the themes of person-centered direct support.

- Think about the theme at the beginning of each day.

- Notice things that happen that show you something important about the theme you are living with.

- Look for occasions to put the theme into action, maybe in a way that is new for you.

- Take a few minutes at the end of the day to review what you have discovered about the theme during the day.

Use the space on this page to summarize the main things you have learned by living with the theme for a week.

We are grateful to Michael Ray, teacher of creativity at the Stanford Business School, for the idea of *Live-Withs*.

Taking pictures of important moments with a disposable camera and making a story board allows people to share and celebrate what they have learned from their efforts to make significant changes.

Raise Expectations

We search out knowledge that will increase our idea of what is possible.

We encourage one another to pursue our dreams.

Jesse Jackson reminds us that all of us count and all of us fit somewhere. This images symbolizes a person reaching for a star which represents their unique purpose and dream for a meaningful life.

Raise Expectations
Manny and Stephanie

Manny is such a different person these days that often people don't even recognize him. When he was a day treatment program client, bused back and forth from home, Manny had no connections or experiences in the community.

Manny now receives the individualized support he needs to live in his own apartment and be active in his neighborhood in Queens.

Manny counts on direct support staff like Stephanie to assist him to find the places where he can become a member, make a contribution, and belong. Stephanie helped Manny move into his apartment and she assists with the practical things involved in managing home life, like shopping and cooking. They also sharing a love for Latino music, drawing and painting.

Manny worked at a restaurant where he made friends who introduced him to a local pool hall. When that pool hall closed, Stephanie helped him find a new place to belong and to play pool.

Manny volunteers at FoodChange, a neighborhood non-profit agency, where he prepares and serves food to homeless people. Over the years, the agency has recognized his dedication with awards.

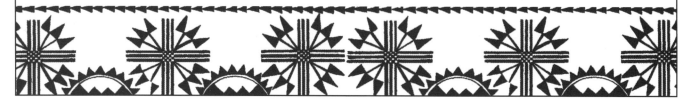

When Manny lost his real family, Stephanie helped him build connections to a surrogate family. He travels independently every day to spend time with them. Stephanie and other staff are helping Manny explore a move that will enable him to live closer to his new family and maybe to work in the dry cleaning business that they operate.

Manny and Stephanie work together to plan out his weekly schedule so that he brings his gifts to community life through positive involvement in a variety of places. As things change over time, Stephanie and Manny make new decisions based on Manny's growing independence and expanding preferences. As Manny develops community relationships and natural supports, Stephanie readjusts the way they spend time together so that he can take greater charge of expanding his life even more. Manny brightens all his relationships with his enthusiasm, and Stephanie keeps him connected to the things that bring life in.

Live-With
Raise Expectations

Live-Withs are calls to attention. Each *Live-With* invites you to focus for one week on one of the themes of person-centered direct support.

- Think about the theme at the beginning of each day.

- Notice things that happen that show you something important about the theme you are living with.

- Look for occasions to put the theme into action, maybe in a way that is new for you.

- Take a few minutes at the end of the day to review what you have discovered about the theme during the day.

Use the space on this page to summarize the main things you have learned by living with the theme for a week.

We are grateful to Michael Ray, teacher of creativity at the Stanford Business School, for the idea of *Live-Withs*.

Listen With Heart

We find ways to see with the eye of our hearts.

We practice clearing away the fear, anger, & hopelessness that block our ability to understand.

We recognize that we can never know all there is to know about a person.

This image symbolizes seeing into other people's hearts and souls with the eyes of the heart. We are more likely to have imaginative vision for people's lives when we see them through the eyes of the heart.

Listen With Heart
Tyesast and Louisa

Tyesast and I went through magazines to find photos of the things she loves. We made a collage out of the pictures to express her interests. We also made a basket to hold items that represent her interests and hopes for the future. Since she does not speak, working with images and objects really helps her communicate. Her unique gift is her smile. She can always put a smile on your face and make you laugh, even if you are feeling really down. She likes to get her hair and nails done, and she loves to dance and do artwork. She expresses her interests by pointing and clapping her hands. Her accomplishments over the past two years have been wonderful. She is much more outgoing, and has learned to express herself, do more for herself, and ask for help. We put a beautiful flower in the basket to represent how she has grown from a seed into a flower.

This service worker provides far more than practical assistance. By participating in artistic creation with Tyeast and the others who know and care about her, Louisa joins the body work of helping someone through the day and the mind work of coordinating activities to the soul work of claiming and celebrating each person's human identity and belonging. Their shared creation is beautiful and ordinary. It depends less on formal artistic training than on the pleasure of using everyday crafts in a sacred way to arrange pictures, to collect meaningful objects, to sew a quilt square that is rich in symbol and story.

The simple act of attention to images and objects that tell the story of what Tyeast loves, and their thoughtful collection into a collage and basket of wonderful things, embodies respect for her interests and helps communicate her identity to people who spend time with her.

A direct support worker who understands her two years of engagement in a person's life as the unfolding of a seed into a beautiful flower has different possi-

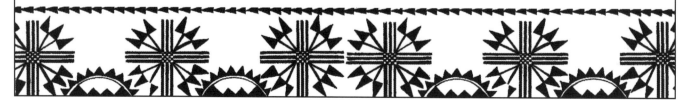

bilities for action than a worker who sees her job only in terms of doing the pre-scribed chores. She can become excited about figuring out how other's can share the beauty and pleasure of Tyeast's interests. She can be alert to the unfolding of new blooms because she knows there has never been a flower quite like Tyeast before.

– Beth Mount, The Art and Soul of Person-Centered Planning

Louisa and Tyeast had another opportunity to create an artifact that tells a story of Tyeast's unfolding. Louisa worked with the staff at Job Path to create a design for a "story square" that expresses the ways that Tyeast's life is unfolding step by step as she becomes more and more independent and involved in community life. Then Louisa and Tyeast worked together with fabric to turn the original drawing into a square for a large quilt that tells the story of the values of the agency. Tyeast and Louisa told the story of the "ladder to Tyeast's dream," at an agency wide open house celebration. Through this process, Tyeast and Louisa have given voice to the meaning of their work together that has strengthened the direction and mission for the whole agengy.

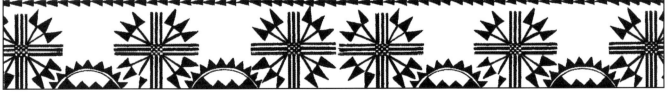

Live With
Listen with Heart

Live-Withs are calls to attention. Each *Live-With* invites you to focus for one week on one of the themes of person-centered direct support.

- Think about the theme at the beginning of each day.

- Notice things that happen that show you something important about the theme you are living with.

- Look for occasions to put the theme into action, maybe in a way that is new for you.

- Take a few minutes at the end of the day to review what you have discovered about the theme during the day.

Use the space on this page to summarize the main things you have learned by living with the theme for a week.

We are grateful to Michael Ray, teacher of creativity at the Stanford Business School, for the idea of *Live-Withs*.

Build Alliances

We invest in others who can make a positive difference. Taking and encouraging positive action is the sign of an alliance.

We are honest in looking for creative ways to deal with conflicts.

The Adinkra symbol for "Nyame" represents the higher powers of awareness. Nyame inside a heart symbolizes overcoming separation and conflict between people, their families, and direct support staff by developing a common vision for the person with a disability.

Build Alliances
Tito and Peter

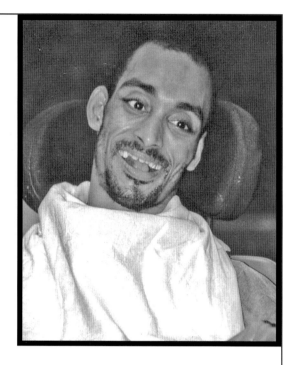

Francisco Rivera, also known as Tito, may seem limited in many ways, but he does a great job expressing himself using hand gestures, facial expressions, picture symbols, and his Dynavox (a communication device). Tito's entire face lights up when he is excited. He uses this light to direct people to work towards the things that matter to him. Peter Dabo has done a wonderful job of listening to Tito, and bringing out his gifts.

In Tito's frequent interactions with police officers he makes it clear that he admires and is attracted to police work. This has led Tito to a strong desire to belong of the Police Department. He has a lot of police friends and visits on a regular basis. He has taken the role of security guard within the building. His support staff are programming his Dynavox so that he can welcome people at the door, and give directions when asked.

Tito is also a businessman. He communicated his desire for his own business by pointing to photos of men in suits with briefcases and to his wallet. Tito has developed a partnership with a local artist and shop owner named James De La Vega, a community activist who makes inspirational and uplifting art. James is the perfect ally and business partner for Tito. Tito sells hats and T-shirts made by De La Vega that say things like "Live Your Dreams." Tito is

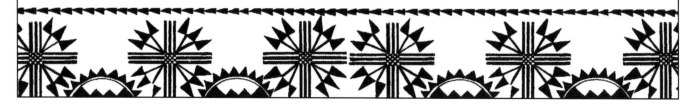

now making business cards to promote his business, named "Urban Chic." His Dynavox now includes price quotes and promotional pitches for his products.

Tito loves music, and has become a regular at local music stores where he buys his compact discs and music cassettes. He carries his CD player everywhere he goes, and makes sure that music fills the room where he is. Tito's desire is to bring beauty into every space he enters.

Speaking of great beauty, Tito has a love of his life. Thanks to Peter, Tito spends regular time with his girlfriend, Wanda, and their friendship has grown into a celebrated romance. Tito thinks of marriange, and perhaps of having a family.

The pictures show an early drawing of Tito's dreams and preferences made by Peter, and then a later translation of that drawing into a story quilt of Tito's dreams coming to life. Tito has been very involved in the design of the artwork, just another way of bringing to light what is meaningful in his life.

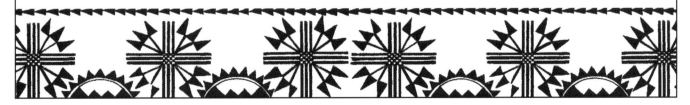

Live-With
Build Alliances

Live-Withs are calls to attention. Each *Live-With* invites you to focus for one week on one of the themes of person-centered direct support.

- Think about the theme at the beginning of each day.
- Notice things that happen that show you something important about the theme you are living with.
- Look for occasions to put the theme into action, maybe in a way that is new for you.
- Take a few minutes at the end of the day to review what you have discovered about the theme during the day.

Use the space on this page to summarize the main things you have learned by living with the theme for a week.

We are grateful to Michael Ray, teacher of creativity at the Stanford Business School, for the idea of *Live-Withs*.

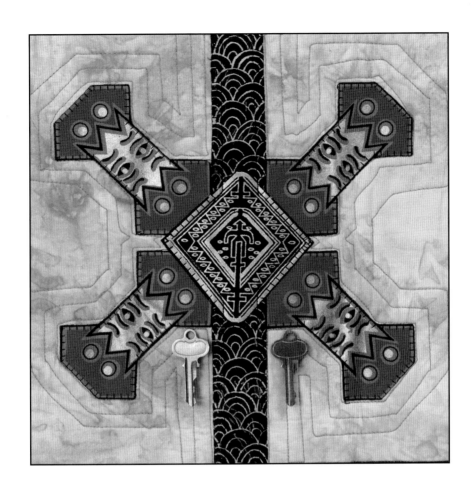

Open Choices

We look for ways to increase opportunities.

We follow people's lead as much as possible.

We assist people to learn from their choices.

This image represents personal empowerment that grows as
one assumes greater control and choice in life. The expanding
arms of empowerment are adorned with keys to symbolize
ownership and authority in one's life.

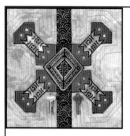

Open Choices
Sam and Camille

Sam's story is a study of finding new keys to life as new people have opened doors to new opportunities.

It all started when Camille, Sam's direct support worker, explored ways to make his upcoming birthday a special event. Sam always talked about "wearing a Tux, and taking a Limo to a big party," so Camille took his dream seriously and decided that Sam needed a man in his life to make this happen.

Sam is also very interested in cars, and car keys, so Camille approached a friend of hers named Squire, who is a Mason and the owner of a car dealership. As fate would have it, the Mason's were about to have a black tie dinner dance, so Squire invited Sam to come and arranged for a limo to pick Sam up.

On the big night, Sam dressed like a million dollars, danced all night with beautiful women, and became "my man Sam" to Squire, who arranged for a birthday cake and for Sam during the dance. Sam was then convinced that the dinner dance was in fact, his birthday party, and his life has not been the same since that enchanted evening.

As a result of Sam's new role as "my man" to Squire, Squire invited Sam to visit the car dealership to work for a day in every department. Sam tried working on the sales floor, the maintenance department, and the service department, with a proper lunch hour in between. Sam decided he liked the work in the service department best, and especially his new service department friends, Nick, Ed, Rene, and Lisa.

Sam asked Squire if he could come back once a week, and Camille worked hard to make all the transportation and scheduling arrangements to make it happen. Sam has now been hired to work in the service department once a week, and he is working to persuade "my man" Squire, to give him more hours. Who knows what will happen next as a result of Camillie finding a key for Sam, and an ally in Squire?

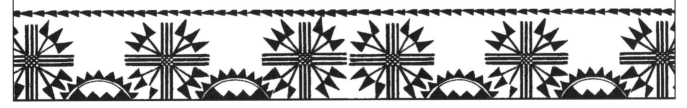

Whose Life Is It, Anyway?

Peter Leidy

I want to address power struggles between staff and people being supported. This is intended as a conversation-starter for direct support workers, to promote discussion of issues staff face while engaged in this important work. You will notice there are questions throughout the paper; these, I hope, will prompt thinking.

My hope is that we can think together about power struggles because it's an important topic and because I believe we get "stuck" on this on a fairly regular basis. Why? Because many people with disabilities rely on provider agencies and/or support staff to help with a host of daily, weekly, and monthly tasks. These "helpers" have a lot to do, and are often under pressure from a variety of sources. Also, historically people with disabilities have wielded little control over their own lives, and although this is changing, the change comes slowly. And power struggles are present in virtually every relationship. There's no avoiding them, so the challenge is to learn how to respond to them.

Back in 1985 I was new to this work of supporting people with disabilities to live in their own homes. I went to work for Options in Community Living, a supported living agency in Madison, Wisconsin. As I tried to learn what Options and my job were all about, (which, to be honest, sometimes involved pretending that I understood more than I did) there was a phrase I'd hear occasionally when staff were talking about the work we do and how they thought about it. "We have to understand that we have power in people's lives," they would say. "We need to have power with people, not power over people."

I found this puzzling at first, because I thought of myself as offering support to help people get what they needed and wanted—not controlling them. I saw my co-workers supporting people rather than exercising power over them. But as I learned more about how the human service system operates, and about many people's vulnerability, I began to understand. And started to look more closely at how we were doing our work with people.

Having power with someone I supported meant to be an ally. Not to always agree, but to support the person with the understanding that it is Bob's life, not mine. It meant realizing that Bob is at risk of living a life directed by others, and my role—our role—at Options was to offer assistance to Bob in a way that would let Bob's life be a reflection of Bob and his hopes and dreams.

Of course, there were disagreements. If Bob chose not to bathe for a prolonged period of time, it would be doing him a disservice for his support staff to simply say, "Well, it's Bob's life, and if he wants to be dirty all the time it's up to him." It could be about hygiene, or how money is spent, or alcohol use, or interpersonal relationships, or umpteen other areas of a person's life. Sometimes we will agree to disagree, but sometimes we can't afford to stop there, because Bob's health or safety might be at risk. These kinds of situations, which arise with great frequency, require us to not only be thoughtful and reflective about our mission and values, but also require us to communicate with each other. Sometimes a lot! With Bob, with our co-workers, a supervisor, perhaps other people important in Bob's life.

As the people with disabilities I was getting to know talked about their lives, I listened to their stories. I learned some history of society's response to disability. This was a history of confinement, of lives being controlled by others, of segregation. People talked about low expectations others had of them, mistreatment, and barriers in the physical world and in other people's minds. We needed to acknowledge the history, to try and understand the control by others that most people with disabilities had experienced, in order for us to make change and do our work purposefully from a place of respect.

As I began to grasp these ideas, I found that it was often easier to think about it theoretically than apply it on a day-to-day basis. It was one thing to say, "I'm not going to control Arlene; she's in control of her own life. I will support her to live the way she wants to live." But it was another thing to realize that Arlene might well live her life—or at least today—in a way that was difficult for me to accept. What happened when Arlene's personality or actions or decisions offended me or irritated me or angered me? After all, I felt a sense of responsibility in her life.

Or this: Arlene's service plan, which is my responsibility to help carry out, contradicts what Arlene is saying she wants to do. A few months ago, Arlene and those of us supporting her all agreed on something, but now as time has gone by Arlene has changed her mind. My role, then, is either going to involve following the previously agreed upon plan, or following Arlene's current wishes which are quite different. To whom am I accountable? Can I get in trouble for not following the plan? Isn't Arlene allowed to change?

These Bob and Arlene questions, it turned out, were what Options team meetings were made of. Usually there were no easy answers, and mostly I found we were working in gray areas. I learned that this kind of work—where gray prevails over black and white—requires a lot of conversation, like talking with, and listening to, Arlene, the important people in her life, and other staff. And I learned that as support staff, we needed to be vigilant about Arlene's "place" in the running of her life. Same with Bob. We needed to ask the question: Whose life is it, anyway?

New questions emerged for us to consider: As we walk side by side with a person we support…

…how can we become (or remain) conscious of their role and our role in small and large interactions or decisions?

…what do we do when power struggles arise?

…how do we know when more than just the person we're supporting needs to have a voice in decision making?

…how do I keep myself from presuming that I know best?

…to what extent do we feel pressure to direct the person?

…what have we learned from co-workers, supervisors, and agency policies about the expectations of our role?

These are some of the questions we need to ask each other in conversations with people we support and the important people in their lives.

Sometimes struggles occur because of personalities or situations where there is no clearly visible reason. And sometimes we are, I think, not even aware that there is a power dynamic going on. For reasons of efficiency, or because we are doing what we think our supervisor or job description dictates, we assume more control in someone's life than is necessary or right. It is often quite subtle: for example, even a simple suggestion we make may carry a lot of weight to a person who feels relatively powerless.

I'd like to say something about the "M" word—manipulation. If I had a nickel for every time I've heard a form of this word as staff talk about their work, I'd be next to Bill Gates on the Forbes list. Okay, I'm exaggerating, but I'd have a couple hundred bucks anyway. "Marilyn is so manipulative." Or, "She'll do anything to get her way." Or, "She likes to play one staff off another."

Sound familiar? This way of talking about people is so common that I think we often fail to look beneath the surface. What might be causing Marilyn to behave this way? Perhaps she feels strongly about something and is simply trying to make it happen using the "tools" at her disposal. What we may perceive as manipulation may really be determination to achieve a desired outcome—to get what she wants.

Most people with disabilities have not experienced balanced relationships when it comes to power. They have tended to have less power and less control in relationships, often being seen for their "deficits" rather then their capabilities. Perhaps a person has been told he can't do something he really wants to do, or needs to do. Knowing what he wants or needs may lead him to pursue his desire in a way that results in the label of "manipulator."

Some people have developed the skill of getting what they want to such a degree that they have earned a reputation as all-star manipulators. The more roadblocks others put up, the better they get at devising ways around them. It reminds me of something I read that is attributed to His Holiness the Dalai Lama: "Learn the rules so you know how to break them properly." I think it is part of human nature to try and get what you believe to be important, whether it is a need or a want. And I think we can learn something from those who are really good at it.

Now, no one likes to feel manipulated by another person. But are we seeing those roadblocks, and questioning why they are there? Think about someone you support, about whom you or others have used the word "manipulation". Think about "power over" versus "power with."

Is it possible that this person lives, or lived for a long period of time, a life where others have more control than she does? Where there are so many rules, regulations, and roadblocks that the person has developed a reputation as a manipulator? What is your role? Are you expected to enforce rules or expectations that she doesn't like or agree with? If so, who made these rules?

Direct support staff play a key role in supporting people with disabilities to build meaningful lives. The quality of this support is enhanced when we make an effort to understand how these relationships are influenced by control and power in people's lives…who should have it and who really does have it.

As we go about our work as individuals, allies, and teams to support and empower people with disabilities to live and work as members of the community, let's keep asking the question: Whose life is it, anyway?

What problems do you think "power over" creates in the relationship between direct support workers and the people they assist?

What pressures do you feel that push you toward "power over" relationships with the people you assist?

What has worked to resist these pressures and practice "power with" the people you assist?

Who else do you want to discuss this paper with?

Live-With
Open Choices

Live-Withs are calls to attention. Each *Live-With* invites you to focus for one week on one of the themes of person-centered direct support.

- Think about the theme at the beginning of each day.

- Notice things that happen that show you something important about the theme you are living with.

- Look for occasions to put the theme into action, maybe in a way that is new for you.

- Take a few minutes at the end of the day to review what you have discovered about the theme during the day.

Use the space on this page to summarize the main things you have learned by living with the theme for a week.

We are grateful to Michael Ray, teacher of creativity at the Stanford Business School, for the idea of *Live-Withs.*

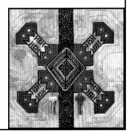

Learn the Neighborhood

We explore from the point of view of the person's (potential) interests.

We become regulars in local places.

This image represents the richness of neighborhood life and the many doors that open for people when we look for opportunities to make connections with them.

Learn the Neighborhood
Julissa and Martha

Julissa is a quiet, loving and friendly young lady who likes to help people in different ways. While she seems very shy at first, she speaks both English and Spanish.

Martha is Julissa's champion, one of the many support workers in her organization who assists people to build connections to their neighborhood based on their preferences.

Julissa has many artistic talents. She loves to paint, draw, sing, and dance. Martha organized an opportunity for Julissa to observe and participate in art classes at York College. Then Julissa took what she learned back to her own community where she helped a group of young people draw objects and scenes from their neighborhoods. They talk as they draw and express their feelings as they work on these activities, just like the professor did in art school. They are writing about their drawings, and the whole process will become an art show that will be displayed at the local library and local bank.

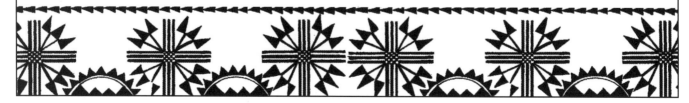

Martha supported Julissa to create three posters of her drawings to symbolize her personal choices.

At a young age, Jullissa told everyone she wanted to be a dancer. For fifteen years she attended a ballet school. Her neighbors and friends know about her dancing talents and invite her to perform every year at the graduation ceremony at Queens Community College.

As a result of Martha's advocacy and action, Julissa now has a paid job three days a week in a nursing home in which many residents are Spanish speaking. The residents appreciate Julissa's loving attention.

Julissa will present her art and her life at a large parent meeting of Spanish speaking parents who have young children with severe disabilities. She wants to show them that all people with disabilities have gifts that they can give their communities when the people around them help them make a path toward their success.

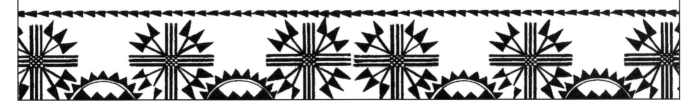

Making Connections: Direct Support Staff as Bridge Builders

Peter Leidy

Community.

Now there's a word we hear often. It's interesting how much the service system uses the word. Community Integration Program, Community Options Program, Adult Community Services, Community Based Residential Facility... you get the idea.

I think the system should use the word community, and of course go beyond words, so that community is actually reflected in the system's response to people with disabilities. I wonder, for a word so often spoken in our work, how much do we really think about what it means?

I would like to think with you about what community might mean in the lives of people with disabilities you support. My hope is that this paper will be a conversation starter: I have some ideas and some questions about what might lead to community membership –or at least produce a spark to start a relationship– and I'm curious what you think.

For now, let's think of community as meaningful relationships with people and places that exist outside the realm of the service system. Some of these relationships are occasional or temporary. Some are, or could be, deeper and long lasting. The possibility of relationship, of interacting with and getting to know someone, is what we're after. If we can at least expand the possibilities, we're on the right track.

Helping make community connections can be intimidating to some people who provide support.

This might sound strange, depending on your point of view. If you're nodding, you know what I mean; if you're puzzled, let me explain. Twenty years ago I was sitting in a roomful of staff. We were listening to a speaker talk about "community building" with adults who have developmental disabilities. Some in the room were excited by this "new" idea –new to most of us anyway. Others were shaking their heads, or wearing concerned expressions. One person said, "I can't do that! I can't even figure out my OWN community connections!" One said, "I'm too shy." Another said, "To be honest, it makes me anxious to try and introduce people to each other, or to ask things of others."

That was twenty years ago, but the wide range of feelings people have about their own ability to do this part of the work is no different today. Many people think only certain "personality types" can be community builders. While it may be true that some have more of a gift or inclination for it than others, we've seen how staff of all stripes can contribute. And THAT is what I want to key into here. The roles that direct support staff have with people put them in a unique position to notice the possibility of a connection, and to help initiate the first steps. From there, it may fizzle out or it may blossom into a wonderful reciprocal relationship. More likely, it will land somewhere in between. But how about testing the waters?

Let's start with the assumption that you work with one, or two, or a few individuals who would benefit from knowing more people who are not paid to be with them. This could mean neighbors, family members, local business owners— the possibilities are many. I think it is safe to assume this because adults with developmental disabilities often have more relationships with paid support providers than they do with non-paid people. This is true even when people are living and working outside of large facilities. Many people are lonely and isolated, and as important as some paid relationships can be, they're no replacement for friends, family, neighbors, and co-workers.

I also imagine that you keep busy in your job and may well feel there's not much time for being a community builder. You work hard, have a lot of responsibilities, have some challenging days, and may feel pressed for time trying to accomplish what is required. So let's focus on what may be a small yet significant role you could have in helping a person make a connection.

Start with how the person spends her time. Here are just a few questions to consider; the idea is to experiment. Where are there currently relationships or potential relationships? Who does she see throughout the week? Does she have a job? If so, where? How does she get there? Is there "down" time on certain days or evenings that could be used more creatively than, say, watching TV? Asking these kinds of questions can prompt some ideas, like building upon an existing acquaintance relationship with someone at work or on the bus.

Periods of leisure or unstructured time may also be a place to begin. There's a difference between going to a movie and going to a neighborhood hangout like a coffee shop. Nothing wrong with movies, there's just not much opportunity to get to know other people. The simple act of introducing the person you support to the shop owner (especially if it's a shop the person would enjoy returning to) could at least lead to one more acquaintance, and who knows—maybe more.

Also, consider the person's interests. What someone finds fun or cool or exciting is often the starting place for exploring connections. Does she like swimming? Gardening? Hip-hop? Being with kids?

Jason, a support worker I know, knew there were a few evenings each week when Don had nothing planned. Since Jason spent that time with Don, he initiated a conversation with Don about some ideas for getting out to have some fun together. Don loves polka music, so Jason did some investigating. He figured, "We're in Wisconsin, this shouldn't be too hard!" Before long, Don was a regular for Monday night polka at Vern's Club, where he met and got to know other polka lovers. They share a common interest and all look forward to Mondays. Notice how this example takes into account both the way Don had been spending his time and an interest he has.

Maybe the person you support sees a certain neighbor several times a week, but does not know the person beyond "Hi." You could help with a next step –and there are many possibilities. Invite the neighbor over for coffee, deliver some fresh-baked cookies, or simply linger a little the next time the "Hi" happens. One small step is still a step in the direction of community, and can make a big difference.

It is also important to remember that the person you've met (neighbor, co-worker, shop owner, etc) may be as interested as the person you support in this new possibility. Community members often say they are glad to be invited into someone's life, and they may not have initiated the contact on their own, for any number of reasons.

These invitations are not the formal, gold-plated type. I'm talking small, casual, friendly –and doable. You're not asking someone to make a big commitment here, at least not yet. Rather, you're helping make it possible for some type of relationship to unfold, which may or may not happen. Again, it is the possibility that's important.

Because of the amount of time and the kind of time you spend with the person, you may be best suited to be a bridge. Direct support staff have the opportunity to get to know people well and be present to watch for the possibilities, whether they are existing relationships that could be deeper, or brand new opportunities. Also, the person may communicate to you, rather than someone else, about an interest she has or someone she'd like to get to know better.

I invite you to think about the role you can have in bridging the gap that often separates people with disabilities from others in the community. Relationships and a greater sense of belonging for a person you support can begin by simply being present, and then taking a small step to encourage the possibilities.

What ideas do you have for acting as a bridge for the people you assist?

Who else would you like to discuss this paper with?

Live-With
Learn the Neighborhood

Live-Withs are calls to attention. Each *Live-With* invites you to focus for one week on one of the themes of person-centered direct support.

- Think about the theme at the beginning of each day.

- Notice things that happen that show you something important about the theme you are living with.

- Look for occasions to put the theme into action, maybe in a way that is new for you.

- Take a few minutes at the end of the day to review what you have discovered about the theme during the day.

Use the space on this page to summarize the main things you have learned by living with the theme for a week.

We are grateful to Michael Ray, teacher of creativity at the Stanford Business School, for the idea of *Live-Withs*.

Let Beauty Shine

We recognize each person's beauty.

We identify and encourage what lets that beauty shine through.

This image represents the beauty inside of people who are valued and respected by the people who care about them. This theme is about the power of supporting people to assume socially valued roles as community members.

Let Beauty Shine
Bob and Clifford

He cannot speak, walk or care for himself, but words give a still voice to his emotions. Bob is a 43-year-old man with cerebral palsy. He was raised in an institution where he was often neglected because he couldn't make his most basic needs known. And, from time to time, he was abused. But Bob is a poet who has learned the power of self-expression.

At age 22, Bob moved into a group home and there he found a supportive staff willing to get to know him. One of the agency's speech therapists discovered that Bob had taught himself to read and designed a communications board that enabled him to better interact with those around him. He uses his right thumb to point to letters and words displayed on his wheelchair's lap-board. The process is laborious for Bob, whose motions are not fluid, and the "listener" needs time and patience.

During the process of person-centered planning, Bob's circle discovered that not only could he communicate but that he had written poetry. The facilitator helped the team to brainstorm ways in which Bob's work could be promoted. At first the planning focused on putting the poems together in an appealing format. Gradually the idea of a book emerged. Other uses for the poems, calendars, cards etc. were also discussed. It was decided to concentrate on copyrighting and publishing a selection of the poems.

Staff then collected his work into an anthology, *Reflections of My Life*, with themes spanning institutional life, the experience of having cerebral palsy and the desire to advocate on behalf of others with disabilities. Cards composed of poems and nature photographs were printed. Another product was also created, Bob's poems were superimposed over nature photographs and matted, ready for framing.

Bob's writing ranges across loneliness, despair, dreams and kindness.

With the aid of the agency's Life Planning Center and his direct support worker, Clifford, Bob has now launched a business venture in order to publish his work. The agency also helped him to obtain a state-of-the-art Dynavox voice synthesizer. Using a wand attached to a headband, Bob points to menus displaying letters, numbers, words and phrases that are translated into digitized "speech." No longer

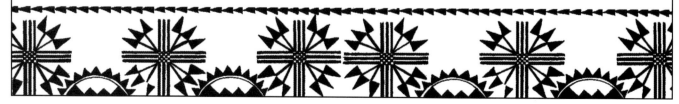

restricted to communicating with individuals who can lean over his lap board, Bob can address large audiences.

"My book is very important to me," says Bob. "I want people to know about me and my work. I want them to understand me better, and I want them to understand cerebral palsy. I am writing for all people with cerebral palsy."

In addition to selling his books, Bob has given poetry readings, and is currently creating material to be used in training professionals about working with people who have disabilities. A short video has been produced about Bob and person centered planning. Bob has presented at a number of local public schools helping young people learn more about disability, showing them how his Dynavox voice synthesizer works, and reading his poetry. He has been a guest speaker at New York University, and he is now working as a consultant for the Speaker's Bureau of the Self-Advocacy Association. With the help of Clifford, his direct support worker, and Ralph from the Life Planning Center, he has launched both his "Handmade Poetry" and his "Abilities Training" consulting businesses.

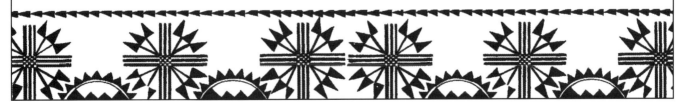

BOY

You have a boy that doesn't see and talk

What are you going to do?

You get aggravated, tired upset.

You try again and again,

You break down and cry,

You help the boy.

How do you feel inside?

You love the boy.

You don't have cold shoulders,

The boy taught you

Don't have cold shoulders.

You open the boy's arms and come inside.

You want to laugh and feel love with the boy.

The boy loves you and cries for you.

The boy questions you, why don't you love him?

You don't turn your back on the boy.

You see the boy's eyes are beautiful.

Eyes tell you, thank you for your help.

– Bob Smith

Live-With
Let Beauty Shine

Live-Withs are calls to attention. Each *Live-With* invites you to focus for one week on one of the themes of person-centered direct support.

- Think about the theme at the beginning of each day.

- Notice things that happen that show you something important about the theme you are living with.

- Look for occasions to put the theme into action, maybe in a way that is new for you.

- Take a few minutes at the end of the day to review what you have discovered about the theme during the day.

Use the space on this page to summarize the main things you have learned by living with the theme for a week.

We are grateful to Michael Ray, teacher of creativity at the Stanford Business School, for the idea of *Live-Withs*.

Support Voice

We find ways to assist communication and use what works in a disciplined way.

We encourage people to say what's important to them and to ask for what they really want. We negotiate.

We learn from honesty, especially when it threatens or angers us

This image symbolizes the liberating potential of effective communication using tools forged from a commitment to listen to and learn from each other.

Support Voice
Ken and Arnie

Ken continues to surprise everyone as his capacity to contribute to community life grows. He and his allies defy the stereotypes and obstacles that could have kept him on the sidelines of life. The old images of Ken as a deaf-blind, self-abusive, profoundly cognitively and medically impaired boy have turned into powerful experiences of Ken as a farmer, a worker, and a fulfilled young man.

Ken works full time at the Adriance Farm in Queens, New York. Every morning, he gathers, washes, dries, and packs the eggs produced by the farm hens. Then Ken assists with other jobs such as feeding the rabbits, weeding, picking ripe tomatoes from the vegetable patch, and watering greenhouse plants.

Ken's world is a busy mix of touch and smell. Arnie, his support worker of five years, facilitates Ken's work and his interactions, guiding his footsteps and his hands. Whenever possible, Arnie moves to the side to allow Ken to act on his own, but they stay closely synchronized with one another in a sort of dance that demonstrates Ken's abilities.

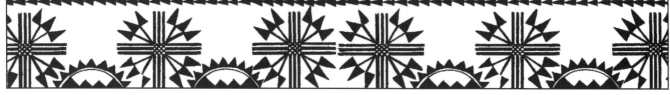

Ken has learned a number of hand signals and signs and Arnie has developed a profound sensitivity to Ken. Arnie knows what Ken likes and how he communicates his feelings and moods. He has learned to anticipate when Ken might be hungry, hurting, or tired. Arnie says, "It's amazing the things that Ken has to go through in a day and the way he adapts. I try to be intuitive and know what he wants. Ken is very receptive to moods. If I have a bad mood it will affect Ken, so I have to stay focused and aware. We have a great relationship, Ken is my best friend. I can tell him everything and he does not judge me! We are very, very close."

Arnie actively supports Ken's relationship with all the other people who work on the farm. Over time, they have developed an understanding of Ken's unique gifts, communication methods, and style of working. Arnie not only tunes in to Ken's inner world, he also builds communication bridges between Ken and all the possibilities and people in the outer world.

Arnie's sensitivity and devotion has helped to transform Ken's life. And, as Arnie will tell you, "My world is a better world because of Ken. Knowing him has changed my life."

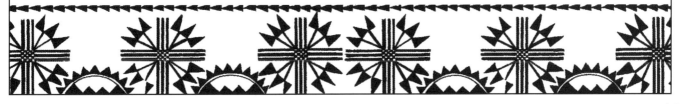

If I Knew Then What I Know Now: Getting Off to a Good Start as a Support Worker

Peter Leidy

I hear it over and over. I heard it fifteen years ago. Ten, five, yesterday. When I talk to direct support staff that have been around for a while, who have made a commitment to keep doing this work, most of them say it in one way or another:

I wish I knew then what I know now.

The first days and weeks on the job are filled with unknowns. Some mysteries just come with the territory, and we can never "know" it all. But I wonder about all the unknowns that are unnecessary—that are unknown because someone forgot to mention something, or key information was neglected in the orientation or initial training. Or, as often happens, was mentioned—once—along with so many other things, and not spoken of again.

It's important to acknowledge that relationships take time; and a lot of what we learn about another person (and our place in his or her life) happens gradually. No one can possibly inform a new employee of everything they need to know right up front, because much of the learning and experiences that will unfold over time have to do with the relationship that is only just beginning.

It takes time to get to know someone, and it takes time to learn a new job. The question is, how long should it take—how long can we afford for it to take—for a support worker to learn some basic and important information about the new job, the new employer, and the person being supported?

Support workers who have made a commitment and stayed a year or two (or ten or twenty) are a valuable resource for new staff. But are they tapped for their insights and knowledge? Here are some ideas from direct support staff about how to help someone get off to a good start. Consider these, and think about what you would add:

Have multiple teachers. Rather than learning about the person, the job, the agency from one or two people, arrange for a variety of people to help bring a new staff member on board. This could include the person supported, family members, friends, other direct support staff, as well as middle or upper management. There may be many people who carry the story of the person—let's benefit from their knowledge.

Have access to "the files." Direct support staff often feel left out of the information loop. A person's written record, flawed though it may be, is part of the information available about the person's history, life experiences, and who they are now. While too often this record is deficit-oriented and excludes an account of a person's gifts and capabilities, it can seem to those on the front lines that they are not important enough to be allowed to review it. Managers sometimes say that this is because "we don't know how long they'll be around." But wait—part of keeping someone around is helping that someone feel included and well informed!

It is worth considering how the person's records could be instructive for new staff. To review this information with someone who knows the person well could offer the opportunity to talk over things like labels (what they do and don't tell us) diagnoses, relationships, the person's "placement" history, etc. There could be a conversation about where this person's experience lies in the history of disability services--for example, "What might it have been like in 1946 when her family faced the choice of institutionalizing her or keeping her at home without enough support?" There are many other topics that a guided review of someone's records could address.

Have a mentor. For all the talk about the benefits of mentoring, surprisingly little is actually done to promote it. It requires a small amount of time and effort to make it happen, but most people involved say it is well worth it. Imagine if (or remember when) you were a new employee. Wouldn't it have been helpful to have someone designated at the same "level" who could act as a guide or resource person for you, to help you learn the ropes?

Create opportunities for me to talk about what I'm learning. Feeling supported helps people stay when the going is tough. Staff should be invited to ask questions and to talk with others, including but not limited to their supervisor. It is helpful for new staff (and for the person they are supporting) for their supervisor or someone else to check in with them in the beginning. When Mark was working his first weekend with Paul and Andy, his supervisor called a couple times simply to check in and see if Mark had any questions. A few minutes of time on Saturday and Sunday made a big difference to Mark.

Emphasize and support teamwork. The best work gets done when individuals have a sense that they are a team member. You may have noticed that corporate America has realized this, and now sales clerks at some big-box stores have the title of "Team Member." Teams are big for a good reason: in many types of work, we work better when we work together. In our work, too often staff feel isolated. It doesn't have to be that way. Recently a long-term direct support worker told me: "You need to feel like you are part of a team…if your supervisor is not supporting teamwork, and the concept of a team, you need to speak up. When you don't feel part of a team, it doesn't feel right, and more things tend to go wrong."

Tell me it's okay to not know everything. One staff person said, "Looking back, I realize how little I knew at the beginning. There were some things that I could have and should have been informed of, but I guess my supervisor forgot…or maybe she didn't know. I felt like it was expected that I should know more than I did. I hesitated to ask because I didn't want to seem incompetent. But now I know that there's a lot you can't know right away. I wish someone had told me it's okay not to know everything."

One agency's direct support staff* are devising a concrete way to help new staff get off to a good start: a tool to elicit information from departing direct support staff in order to capture their knowledge and experiences about the person(s) being supported. Here are some of their questions:

What do you know about Martha's personal/family history?

How does Martha express herself?

Do you have any specific suggestions to improve communication with or about Martha?

Are there any special interests or hobbies that you've learned are important to Martha? What role can staff play in helping Martha pursue them?

What personal characteristics or tendencies of Martha do you think it's important for a new person to know about?

(Thanks to Options in Community Living in Dane County, WI for sharing this.)

To this list I would add:

Who are important people in Martha's life?

Have you noticed any newer relationships that you think Martha might like support to pursue?

What have you learned about Martha's daily rhythm?

Do you have any suggestions about improving Martha's support?

Looking back, what would have been helpful to know when you started working with Martha?

Taking the time to gather this information benefits both Martha and her incoming support workers. It also shows respect to the outgoing staff, who too often are not asked to share their knowledge and ideas.

What questions would you add to those above?

What can you do to share your unique and important perspective about someone you support?

Live-With
Support Voice

Live-Withs are calls to attention. Each *Live-With* invites you to focus for one week on one of the themes of person-centered direct support.

- Think about the theme at the beginning of each day.

- Notice things that happen that show you something important about the theme you are living with.

- Look for occasions to put the theme into action, maybe in a way that is new for you.

- Take a few minutes at the end of the day to review what you have discovered about the theme during the day.

Use the space on this page to summarize the main things you have learned by living with the theme for a week.

We are grateful to Michael Ray, teacher of creativity at the Stanford Business School, for the idea of *Live-Withs*.

Celebrate Community

We get involved and encourage others to get involved in what's happening in community life.

We support local businesses and associations.

We find ways to help out those people who work hopefully for a stronger community.

This image represents the richness of neighborhood life and the many doors that open for people when we look for opportunities to make connections on their behalf.

Celebrate Community
Joe and Mavis

Joe has a whole new life since he became an active member of a church community where he has become a member of the choir, a friend to the pastor, the person who hands out bulletins,

and an active participant in every possible church celebration and special occasion.

This transformation is significant because Joe was once seen as so violent that most staff did not want to get near to him. Fortunately for Joe, Mavis, his direct support worker, saw him in a different light and recognized his deep desire to be a member of a spiritual community. Mavis introduced Joe to her own church, and he gradually became involved.

Mavis supported Joe to form a bond with the parishioners and they became his extended family, inviting him to birthday and family parties and special events at the church. He has been asked to pray and sing in many services. Joe has his special place to sit at church, and all the members are quite protective of it. They ask for him when he is absent, and Joe also notes when anyone is missing and asks for them.

With Mavis' help, Joe memorizes the topic and scripture verse for each service. Joe has developed a very close bond with the pastor.

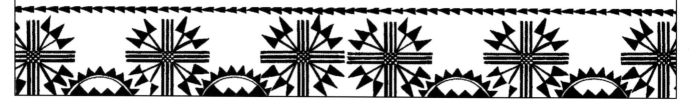

Mavis has also helped Joe contact a family member, whom he invited to go to church with him. This family member was concerned that Joe was overmedicated because she had never seen him so calm. Staff were happy to report that his medications have actually been decreased. He has become much happier and much more expressive of his feelings and so he does not become aggressive. He is a new man as a result of Mavis' divine imagination and human concern.

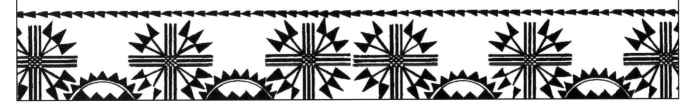

Live-With
Celebrate Community

Live-Withs are calls to attention. Each *Live-With* invites you to focus for one week on one of the themes of person-centered direct support.

- Think about the theme at the beginning of each day.

- Notice things that happen that show you something important about the theme you are living with.

- Look for occasions to put the theme into action, maybe in a way that is new for you.

- Take a few minutes at the end of the day to review what you have discovered about the theme during the day.

Use the space on this page to summarize the main things you have learned by living with the theme for a week.

We are grateful to Michael Ray, teacher of creativity at the Stanford Business School, for the idea of *Live-Withs*.

Nurture Relationships

We offer, look for and appreciate hospitality.

We encourage next steps in friendship.

We actively assist people to stay in touch with important others.

We support reconciliation

This image represents the circle of relationships through which people are connected to community life. The center five pointed star represents the valued experiences that come from community inclusion: having respect, sharing places, making a contribution, making choices, and knowing people.

Nurture Relationships
John and Thomas

John moved out of his family home and into our residence, and he was really having trouble getting adjusted and getting along with other people. He behaved very differently when his father was around, and we realized how much he missed his dad, but his father could not visit every day.

So I decided that I would become a surrogate father for John by building a strong bond with him and his father. I hoped this would satisfy his need for a close relationship, and help him realize that he could trust other people besides just his dad.

To start building the relationship, I spoke with John and his dad about John's interests, and learned more about his love of music. I brought him CDs and we listened to them together both on our own and when his dad came to visit. I tried to be involved in his visits with his father as much as possible, and I learned a lot about the family, their lives, and interests.

As time went on, I gained John's trust and became a bridge to John and other members of the community. He became much more social and involved in community life. He began to build his CD collection, and spend more time in the community listening to music.

This change began from the first time we just shared our love of music. I do believe that he understood that I cared about him, and wanted his life to be better. His quality of life is much better and it makes me feel great to know that I helped.

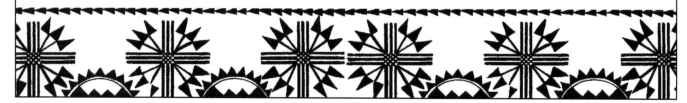

Live-With
Nurture Relationships

Live-Withs are calls to attention. Each *Live-With* invites you to focus for one week on one of the themes of person-centered direct support.

- Think about the theme at the beginning of each day.
- Notice things that happen that show you something important about the theme you are living with.
- Look for occasions to put the theme into action, maybe in a way that is new for you.
- Take a few minutes at the end of the day to review what you have discovered about the theme during the day.

Use the space on this page to summarize the main things you have learned by living with the theme for a week.

We are grateful to Michael Ray, teacher of creativity at the Stanford Business School, for the idea of *Live-Withs*.

Your Learning Journey

The way to increase your ability to assist people to act as a contributing citizen is to do it in a thoughtful way. As Antonio Machado's poem says, the path into a more satisfying life can only be made by walking it, stopping from time to time to reflect and take stock of what you have learned and what the possibilities for interesting next steps might be.

Even though this may be a short journey when measured in miles, it can seem like a very long way when people have to walk through the walls that separate people with disabilities from everyday opportunities. One of our friends, who is a fan of Star Trek likes a sticker that she found for her wheelchair. The outer space explorers on Star Trek "boldly go where no one has gone before." Her sticker says, "To boldly go …where everyone else has already been." Just going across the street can take courage when it means upsetting a comfortable routine and confronting the possibility that others will react with prejudice instead of welcome.

This is a map of the learning journey you and your partner will take together. As you can see, this is not a shortest, straightest

Make an agreement to learn together ⟶ Try something new in the community

- Organize information
- Make a plan
- Make connections
- Adjust assistance as needed

Ask "What's working?"

Ask "How do we build on what's working?"

Ask "What are we learning?"

Tell the story of what you are learning

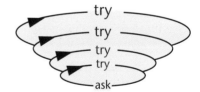

The journey has a spiral shape. Each time you go around the try and ask circle, you have the choice of moving on to the next, wider circle.

route kind of trip. It is a journey of exploration. The point of the journey is not to make a plan on paper. The point of the journey is to make a path into community contribution by walking (or rolling) together into new places and new roles.

Make an agreement

This is not a journey that you can take alone. You need a partner, a person with a disability who is willing to try new things with your assistance. And you need a learning buddy, a person you trust to help you reflect on what you are doing and how you might do it better; a person who can help you keep the purpose of the journey clearly in sight, especially when things get tough. Your buddy doesn't need to be part of the action; your buddy needs to be available from time to time to help you think things through. Choose someone you respect and trust and ask them if they will make some time for you. Start with a conversation about who to ask to be your learning partner.

If you have doubts about taking the journey, review page 16.

You reach the first milestone when you choose a partner and make an agreement to learn together. What matters is that you have or can build a relationship that allows both of you to try something that has a chance of bringing something good into the person's life. Other direct support workers have taken these journeys with people whose communication, or movement, or self-control is very limited, so don't let a person's apparent disability stop you from asking them to join you.

You might think that you cannot communicate well enough with the people you assist to allow you to join them in a learning journey. This might not be so. A person you can't understand yet could be a great partner on a journey that will demand your careful attention to all of the ways the person might communicate and your sensitive imagination to discover capacities and connections. Even if the steps turn out to be small, the rewards for both of you could be big.

As you think about asking the person to join you on your learning journey, consider what you know about the person.

- Where and when does the person feel most comfortable about thinking about new possibilities?

134

- What is the best way for the person to take in information?
- How does the person usually make decisions (Does the person usually jump right in, or take time to think it over, or say no quickly and then say yes, or…)?
- Is this the kind of decision the person can make on their own or do you also need to talk to the person's guardian or another adviser? (Even if the person counts on a guardian, be sure and ask the person to agree. If their communication with you is limited, ask them to let you know if they agree in the best way they can.)

Remember, you are asking the person to help you, but they have a good chance of benefiting. You will be better able to help people and they will get to try some new things, some of which may turn out to be enjoyable and interesting. Before agreeing, the person should know…

… that you want to learn to be a better assistant by working with them to try something new that they will enjoy.

… that the person can say no, either to the whole idea or to any of the steps along the way.

…that you will be telling your learning buddy (and maybe others if you are part of a class or a learning group) about what you are doing and what you are learning; you will not tell other people anything that the person has not heard and given permission to share.

…about how often you will get together to plan or try things

…what the arrangements are about money (e.g. admission costs, meals or snacks, dues or fees) and transportation.

Once you have your partner and your learning buddy, the journey can begin. Be sure to put specific times in your schedule to organize information about the person and the community, make plans, and make connections. Review the check list on page 13 to see if you need to negotiate with your supervisor or your co-workers to get support for your learning journey.

Try something new

The basic pattern for trying something new in the community is simple to describe:

Identify a capacity in the person	→	Identify a place in the community where that capacity is welcome	→	Make the connection	→	Arrange assistance & adjust as needed

Sometimes this pattern moves in small steps that slowly build on one another. Sometimes it moves more quickly and in bigger steps.

A journey in smaller steps

To learn from a journey of small steps that build to bigger changes, meet Martin.* His journey with Anna began from a simple capacity: his delight in buying snacks from the day program vending machine and his ability to spend small amounts of pocket money on them. Within the walls of the day program, this small capacity was simply the way to a treat. Anna looked again and saw this small capacity as a possible passport to a bigger world. Carefully, she assisted Martin to buy his snack at a local store. In his small step by small step movement from refusing to get out of the van to feeling the confidence to pick and pay for his snacks, Martin quietly and without words recruited Sandra, a store clerk, as his ally. This led to a next step, stocking shelves in exchange for merchandise, and a next step, stocking shelves for pay.

Some people don't like working for change and resist learning from stories of change by accenting the differences between people who make a positive change and their ideas of the people that they support. There are real differences, but there is also much to learn. This learning doesn't happen when people think of Martin and Anna's journey from the vending machine to stocking shelves in a community store as a matter of luck. Luck might enter in, but mostly it is thoughtful, careful, hard work. It is lucky that Sandra was willing to become part of their journey and that the store manager was open to Martin's connections to the store. It is possible to imagine a different store, one whose clerks are so busy, or prejudiced, or turn-over so rapidly that they would have no time for Martin. It is possible to imagine a different Martin, one who

* All of the names in this example have been changed..

stubbornly clings to his fear and refuses forever to leave his seat in the van. But that is not the store or the Martin that Anna worked to bring together. Sandra and the store were there whether Martin was present or not. Their potential to bring good things into Martin's life depends on connection. Anna was the midwife for the connection, using her skill to build Martin's confidence and her creative attention to encourage and build positive contact. Martin and his new allies could then do the rest. Luck had help.

Regular place

Regularly buying a snack in a community store

Regular connection

Connecting with the store clerk

Valued role

Employee stocking shelves

Thoughtful assistance

A journey in bigger steps

To learn from a journey that began with bigger, quicker steps, meet Alex, a young woman who lives in Spanish Harlem. On graduation from high school, Alex wanted part time office work, had a record of successful work experience while in high school, and lived across the street from an accessible community center that was willing to hire her. Her interest and capacity were clear and a welcoming place was only a short roll away. It took a few hours of collaborative work to scout for suitable places and figure out how to deal with her needs for assistance. Once she started work, it took some creative thinking to see how this first connection could lead on to others and some careful problem solving and negotiation to deal with the situation when her health took a turn for the worse.

Simple doesn't mean automatic. Some people might have gotten stuck in a deficiency view and been stopped by Alex's sensory and mobility impairments or her chronic health problems. But Alex had the active support of her family and benefited from some highly focused support from people who...

...took her interest in an office job seriously

Remember

The art of discovering...

...what people can contribute to community life

Capacity Thinking

...ways that people can make their contribution

…had confidence in the ability of all the people involved to figure out and implement effective ways to deal with her needs for assistance

…believed that it was possible to find a welcoming place and negotiate a connection outside the boundaries of the human service system

…were able to support the people involved to responsibly take the risks involved in asking for a job and asking for what she needed in order to be successful on the job

It is lucky that Alex could communicate what she wanted to do, but luck needs help from people who practice respect if people are going to hear and act on what she has to say. It is lucky that this young woman already had work experiences that prepared her for the available job, but luck needs help from people with high expectations if her ability is going to translate into a paycheck. It is lucky that there was a welcoming workplace right across the street, but luck needs help from people who practice capacity thinking if people are going to notice an opportunity and then pursue it.

You can decide to be the help that your partner's luck needs. This does not guarantee success, but it is necessary to the journey.

Deepen relationships with family & friends

Make connections in the neighborhood

Make contributions through paid work & volunteering

Build membership through associations

Strengthening hope and courage

Both Martin and Alex took positive steps because they had active support to identify and organize the capacities available to them from the interaction between their own abilities and interests, their allies, their neighborhood, and the service system. Noticing capacities and taking action depend on how strongly they were lifted by hope and courage instead of being squashed by doubt and fear.

Hope and courage exist in a balance with doubt and fear. In the right balance, doubt and fear play a positive part by alerting us to potential problems and concerns that are worth working on. But doubt and fear lock people in. Those who simply work to avoid their nightmares will make little progress toward their dreams. It takes hope and courage to find the way to make the best of any situation that people face.

To achieve goals you've never achieved before, you need to start doing things you have never done before.

–Steven Covey

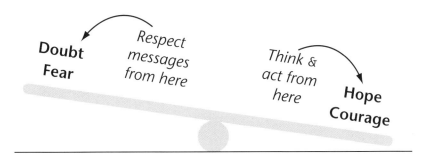

Make Hope and Courage the Strongest Influence

What strengthens hope and courage?

- Taking what the person tells you seriously enough to join them to act on it.
- Seeking out other people who are farther along the journey to act as a contributing citizen and learning from them.
- Looking for opportunities outside the boundaries of human service programs.
- Acting from confidence in people's willingness and ability to be welcoming and to solve problems and overcome difficulties.
- Deciding to ask for what really matters to the person and to speak out clearly when you think opportunities might be missed or lost.
- Sharing responsibility for making good things happen.

Organizing knowledge and making a plan

Because you are trying something new, you need to take action on purpose. Acting on purpose means taking time with your partner to gather and organize what you know from the point of view of discovering new opportunities for your partner to act as a contributing citizen. You need to organize knowledge to answer three questions:

1. **What capacities does my partner have?** Capacities may be...

   - **Gifts of the hand** –abilities and skills that my learning partner can contribute
   - **Gifts of the head** –knowledge, questions, experience, and information that my partner can contribute
   - **Gifts of the heart** –interests, enthusiasms, personal passions, and the rewards of relationship that my partner brings to others.
   - **Gifts of history and identity** – experiences, knowledge, duties, responsibilities, concerns, possibilities for belonging that come with membership in my partner's particular family, religion, national or ethnic group, citizenship

2. **Where in the community will these capacities be welcome?**
   - Which associations and networks of individuals share my learning partner's interests, enthusiasms and passions?
   - Who cares about what my learning partner cares about and how does their caring show up in community life?
   - Where will people identify with my partner's family, nationality, ethnic group, or religion?
   - Who would enjoy my partner's company?
   - Where could my partner's presence make a positive difference?
   - Who would enjoy and add to the knowledge, questions, experiences, and information my learning partner has?
   - Which community projects and activities would benefit from what my learning partner can do or produce?

3. **What will it take for my partner to act as a contributor?**
   - What roles could my learning partner take?
   - How do new people typically join in? Does my partner need any accommodation in joining? Would my partner benefit from someone who is already involved as a sponsor or mentor? If so, who might this be?

Those who simply work to avoid their nightmares will make little progress toward their dreams. It takes hope and courage to find the way to make the best of any situation.

140

- Is any equipment or any particular clothing needed? Are there any fees or expenses?
- How will my learning partner get to and from the places involved? How will any necessary arrangements be made?
- Are there any particular accessibility requirements? What needs to be done to meet them?
- Does my learning partner have any particular communication requirements? What needs to be done to meet them?
- Are there any particular safety or health requirements? What needs to be done to meet them?

Sometimes all of the knowledge you need for the next cycle of trying something new is easily available. The person's capacities are clear, the places and people that offer an opportunity are known, and the person requires very little extra to try the new opportunity. It can be easy to meet a person's requirements for assistance if you or somebody who knows the person's routines is going along. If this is how it is, you can organize the information and make a plan with only a short conversation, a note or two on the to-do list and the calendar, and maybe a visit or a phone call to check things out.

If things are right to try something new in the community with only a little planning, our advice is, do it! The point is to create a new experience of acting as a contributing citizen, not to gather information or make plans for their own sake. Invest only as much time in organizing what you know and planning as you need to.

Maxie, a direct support worker who participated in a learning journey, tells this story about moving immediately from idea to action to a positive change in a person's skills and schedule.

*I was meeting Steven for the first time and decided that doing one of the maps together could help me get to know him. I found out that **he wanted to work on computers at the library. We just got up and went to the library!** I also learned he was interested in music, so while we were at the library we looked up his favorite radio station on the Internet and printed out information. In the process Steven met a library worker, learned how to access the computer, and how to find information. He stayed on the computer for two hours! Now he goes to the library every Wednesday at 11:00 am. This was a great activity for Steven. He*

Take more time to plan when:

- Agreement is lacking among key people
- Capacities are not clear in the person or in the community
- Links to the community are missing
- New ways to assist need to be designed and implemented

Important messages to Steven

Someone is listening.

What you say can lead straight to action.

There are helpful people in community places.

You can gather information that is good to have.

You can learn new things and grow in knowledge and skill.

I'm excited by what we have done.

doesn't get out much, and he had not been to the library in his neighborhood for several years. He has learned his way around the library, he has learned to use the library printer and to log onto different web sites for information, and to ask library workers for help when he needs assistance. I want to invite his parents along so they can see how capable Steven has become!

After each new thing you and your partner try, invest a few minutes in talking about the experience:

- What was good about what we tried?
- What didn't you like about what we tried?
- What went better than we thought it would?
- What didn't go the way we thought it would?
- Do we want to try it again? Why or why not?
- If you don't want to try another time, how do we need to update our understanding of your interests?
- What will we do differently next time?

Talking through these questions is important even if the person has no desire to repeat the activity. By getting very specific about what the person liked and didn't like, you can get clearer about the person's interests. By thinking about what worked and what didn't turn out, you can get more focused about the person's requirements for success.

Sometimes key people don't see the need for change. Sometimes a person's capacities are not clear. Sometimes it is not obvious where or in what ways the person could act as a contributing citizen. Sometimes the ways to assist a person in community settings are not within easy reach. Then you will need to invest more time in gathering information, gathering knowledge, and planning. You can use the worksheets on the following pages to guide you.

Although the dream may be ambitious and failure is a possibility, most people would rather try and fail than not have the opportunity to try at all. And often the journey results in many positive developments, even if the dream is not realized in exactly the way it was envisioned.

–Cathy Ludlum

Relationships are the foundation for gathering useful information and making good plans. Ask yourself whether you need to spend some time getting to know your partner by sharing places and activities that are familiar and comfortable for them.

You may be able to gather the information and make the plans you need by just thinking with your partner, but usually it's a good idea to involve more people. More people bring more different kinds of knowledge and connections. You can gather and organize information by talking to people one at a time or by bringing people together to meet. Working in a group can generate more ideas and make it easier to negotiate commitments, but if people have a hard time working together it might take a skillful group leader to get results.

Remembering why

The purpose of the learning journey is for you to become a better assistant by supporting your learning partner to act as a contributing citizen. You are looking for positive connections between your learning partner and opportunities in the community outside the human service world. These opportunities offer your partner a good chance of increasing their share of the good things in life, including these valued experiences.

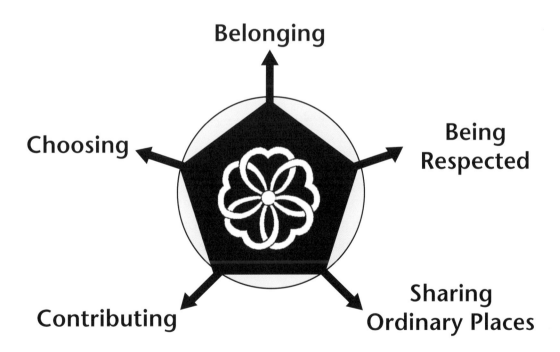

Preparing for the Journey

The Learning Journey

1. Organize knowledge

    My people

    My style

    My places

    My gifts

2. Express capacities

3. Make connections

4. Adjust assistance

5. Tell the story

There are worksheets and instructions for tasks that others have found helpful as they pursued their learning journey. The learning journey has five major steps:

1. Organize knowledge about the person;

2. Express the person's capacities;

3. Make community connections;

4. Adjust assistance;

5. Tell the story.

You can do as many tasks as you find helpful. Or you can invent your own ways to gather and organize knowledge and make connections. Take some time to read through the nine tasks and select those you think will be helpful. You can always drop one task or pick up another as needed.

The tasks are intended to be done with your learning partner and with other people who know and care about your learning partner. Most people enjoy them. If your learning partner doesn't want you to talk to other people about one or another of the topics, respect their choice. If you are unable to communicate with your learning partner, we still strongly recommend that you tell your learning partner what you have found out from your own experiences and from interviewing others. People often understand a great deal even if they have difficulty being understood.

Think about which tasks to do with a group of people and which you will do in one-on-one interviews. Be guided by your learning partner's choice.

One good way to help you tell the story of your learning journey is to take pictures as you go along. Be sure to get whatever permission you need to take pictures and show them to other people. If you don't have a camera, think about buying a single use-camera.

5. Tell the Story

Change	Who	First Step

4. Adjust Assistance

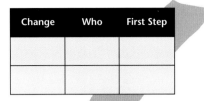

Capacity	Opportunity	Role

3. Make Connections

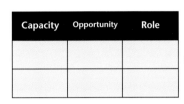

2. Express Capacities

Gifts

1. Organize Knowledge

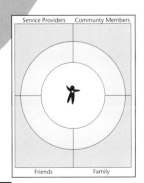

Works	Doesn't Work

Who I am – My People

Use the diagram on the facing page to identify the important people in your partner's life. The circles describe how close people are to your partner; the boxes identify a person's role.

*Put people's names in the white circle at the middle if they are **allies**: people who know your partner well and are willing to work with your partner to make life better. These people hold your partner in their hearts. Some of these people may be family members, some may be friends (with or without disabilities), some may be service providers; the rest are community members.*

*Put people's names in the light grey circle if they are **potential allies**. People who have some relationship with the person but have not yet made a commitment to take positive action with the person. Some of these people may be family members, some may be friends (with or without disabilities), some may be service providers; the rest are community members.*

*Put people in the grey area toward the edge if they have a **potential relationship** with the person. These might be family members the person has not met or had contact with in a long time. They might be friends or service workers from the past who have lost touch. They might be community members (with or without disabilities) who recognize the person but don't yet have a personal relationship.*

Draw a heart next to those whom your learning partner cares about most deeply.

Draw a star next to those who know an important part of your partner's story.

Put a circle around people who know lots of other people in the community.

Put a check mark next to the people you most want to involve in planning and taking your learning journey.

List five things below that will strengthen existing relationships. Ask: What would build even more energy and commitment among the person's allies? What would it take to invite at least one more person to move into the allies circle? What would it take to invite at least one more person to move from the edge of your partner's life into a stronger relationship? How can this learning journey draw strength from and strengthen these relationships.

To do to make these relationships stronger

-

-

-

-

-

Reflection: What we learned from making this relationship map...

Service Providers   Community Members

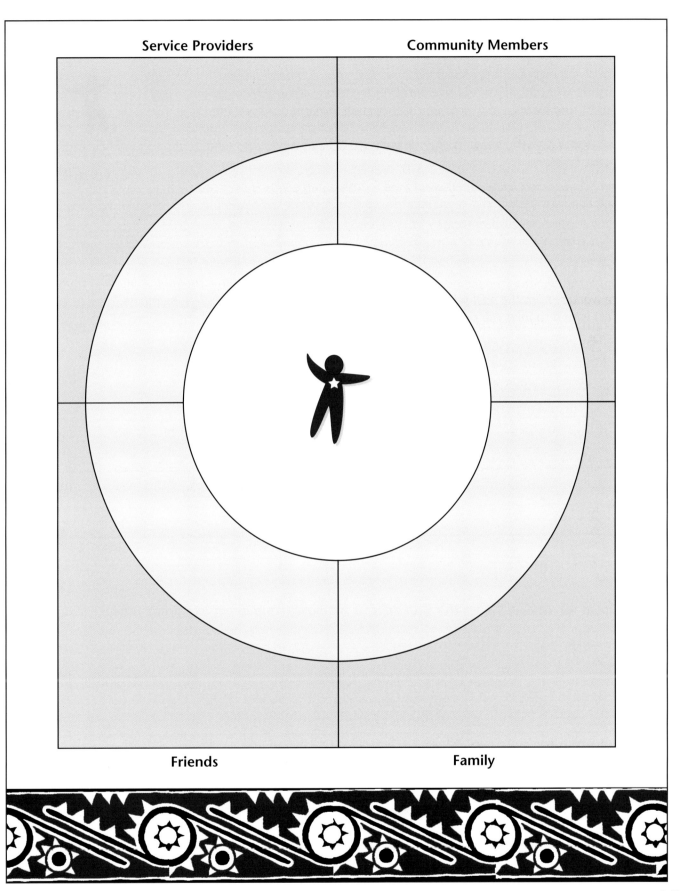

Friends   Family

Who I am – My Style

Your partner, like everyone else, has a personal style that can be described by contrasting what usually works to create engagement, pleasure, energy, and aliveness and what usually creates disconnection, frustration, boredom, and deadness. Use the worksheet on the next page to collect statements from the person and those who know the person well about what works and what doesn't work for them.

In the first pair of boxes think about what your learning partner's experience says about everyday life when it is going particularly well (things are working) and when it is going badly (things are not working).

Then focus on what experience says about what works and what doesn't work when your partner is trying something new.

Then think about what experience shows assists your partner in communicating and in thinking about important matters.

Looking at the whole worksheet, how could we summarize what it says about your learning partner in a few words or phrases? *(for example, "morning person", "high energy", "takes things easy", "no surprises", "loves commotion and noise", "everything goes better with music")*

What should we remember from this worksheet as we move along in our learning journey?

| What works
Usually creates engagement, pleasure, energy, aliveness | What doesn't work
Usually creates disconnection. frustration, boredom, deadness |
|---|---|
| | |

When trying new things

To support communication and thinking

Who I am – My Places

Use the worksheet on the facing page to identify the places that matter in your learning partner's life. Some of these will be everyday places, others might be once-in-a-while places (maybe vacation locations or holiday family visits). Some of these may be community places that your partner goes as an individual. Some may be community places your partner goes as a member of a human service group (maybe a work crew or to the mall or the movies as an activity with staff and fellow group home residents). Some may be human service places (like a day program).

You are looking for ways to understand your learning partner better, not necessarily to make the most complete list possible. Focus on the places that matter, and ask follow-up questions such as "What do you do here?" and "What is it that you like (or don't like) about this place?" It can sometimes help build understanding to get more specific, "You like going to camp, what place at camp is your favorite?"

After you have identified places, think about the role your learning partner plays there.

- *Put an "R" next to community places where your learning partner is a regular customer or browser (maybe a coffee shop or a bookstore or a tavern or a library).*

- *Put an "M" next to community places where your partner is a member (maybe a church or an informal "breakfast club" at a restaurant, or a work group, or the place an advocacy group meets).*

- *Draw a heart next to one or two places that your learning partner most likes to be and feels most himself or herself.*

- *Draw a star next to any community places where you think there are possibilities for making stronger connections.*

Looking at the whole worksheet, how could we summarize what it says about my learning partner in a few words or phrases?

Reflection: What did we learn by identifying the places that matter to my learning partner?

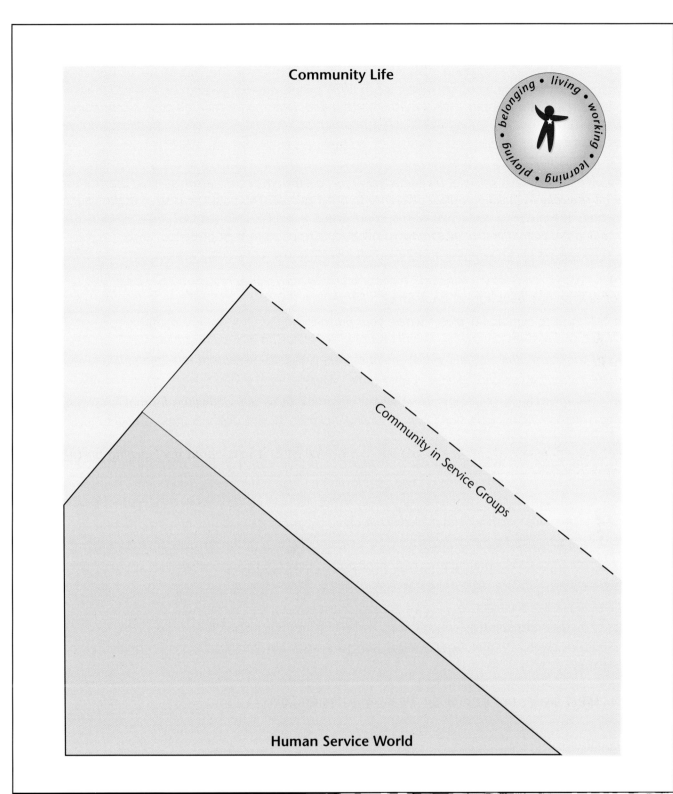

Community Life

belonging • living • working • learning • playing

Community in Service Groups

Human Service World

Who I am – My Capacities and Gifts

*Ask your learning partner to tell you **a story about a time when he or she was at his or her very best**, a time when he or she made a positive difference to other people and felt good to be involved in doing so. It can be a small thing or a big thing, what matters is that your learning partner felt good about doing it. (If you cannot communicate well enough with your learning partner to hear their story, the next step will be even more important.)*

Ask two or three other people who know and care about your learning partner to tell a story about your learning partner when he or she is at his or her very best, a time when the person seemed most himself or herself and were able to make a positive difference to other people. This could be a story about your learning partner doing something actively and on purpose, but it could be a story about the way your learning partner made a positive difference by the way other people respond to their presence.

Reflect on each story by asking, What qualities or gifts does this story show my learning partner to have? *Put a word or a few words where they seem to belong on the diagram on the facing page to identify your learning partner's gifts. Ask, "Are there any other gifts or capacities that aren't in the story?" Add the answers.*

Think about:

- ***Gifts of the hand*** *(and feet and voice) –abilities and skills that my learning partner can contribute (for example: recognizing people and remembering names, dancing, fixing things, singing, typing, drawing, arranging shapes and colors, using a computer, decorating, acting, composing music, figuring out the best way to do a job, sewing, working hard using physical strength, decorating, ability to sign, ability to speak or understand another language)*

- ***Gifts of the head*** *–knowledge, questions, experience, and information that my partner can contribute (for example, figuring people out, organizing and classifying things, travel routes, sports news, fan information, gossip, local history, ability to spot a bargain, ability to debate, sales ability, creative thinking, math, solving puzzles, interest in politics, desire to think and talk about big questions)*

- ***Gifts of the heart*** *–interests, enthusiasms, personal passions, and the rewards of relationship that my partner brings to others (for example, welcoming people, patience, courage, impatience to move from talk into action, sensitivity to others, high energy, desire for order, ability to listen, passion for justice, love of nature, ability to draw others out, spiritual gifts)*

- ***Gifts of history and identity*** *– experiences, knowledge, duties, responsibilities concerns, types of belonging that come with membership in my partner's particular family, religion, national or ethnic group, citizenship*

Reflection: What we learned by naming these capacities and gifts

153

Expressing Who I Am

There is power in creating an artistic expression of a person's interests, capacities, achievements, or visions. This might be...

...a drawing made with markers or crayons that captures images important to the person *(story on page 97).*

... a collage made from images cut out of construction paper or pictures and images cut from magazines *(story on page 76).*

...a basket that holds objects that represent valued qualities of the person and the person's hopes *(story on page 89)*

...an assemblage of words, pictures, and objects that highlight important accomplishments and personal capacities.

...a quilt square that celebrates an important symbol *(story on page 93)*

...a patchwork that translates a sketch into fabric art *(story on page 76)*

...a quilt that uses iron-on photos to capture meaningful moments *(story on page 97)*

... **whatever your imagination leads you to create.**

Use the space on the next page to sketch some of your ideas for expressing an important message about who your learning partner is.

What Connections Am I Looking For?

Review what you know about your learning partner, including what you have learned from the **Who I Am** *worksheets you have done together.*

You are looking for possible connections that could answer one or more of these questions:

- *Which associations and networks of individuals share my partner's interests, enthusiasms and passions?*
- *Who cares about what my partner cares about and how does their caring show up in community life?*
- *Where will people identify with my partner's family, nationality, ethnic group, or religion?*
- *Who would enjoy my partner's company?*
- *Where could my partner's presence make a positive difference?*
- *Who would enjoy and add to the knowledge, questions, experiences, and information my partner has?*
- *Which community projects and activities would benefit from what my partner can do or produce?*

Use the table on the facing page to…

- *In column one, summarize the capacities to build on or develop.*
- *Brainstorm as many possibilities as you can in columns two and three by asking "Where would these capacities be welcome?" and "In what role could the person contribute?" (Roles include such possibilities as security guard, motivational speaker, organizer, soprano, usher, regular patron, waiter, gardener). The ground rule for brainstorming is, "No judgements" – don't worry about whether an idea seems "realistic" or not; sometimes far-out ideas lead on to better ideas and real positive steps.*
- *Review the worksheet and circle two or three of the most promising possibilities.*

Describe as clearly as possible exactly what it is that you are looking for in the community *(for example, "We want to connect with a theatre group that does musicals and will give chorus parts to people who can't read music." or "We want to find a good place to listen to Irish music." or "We want to connect with a group that gives volunteers safe ways to help homeless people." or "We want to connect with an artist who will be a mentor." Be courageous and optimistic: if you don't know what you are looking for, you have little chance to find it; if you don't ask for exactly what you want the chances of getting it are poor.*

What are five positive next steps toward making the connections we are looking for?

-
-
-
-
-

Capacities to Build On or Build-Up	Potential Community Opportunities	Possible Roles
Gifts of hand, head, heart, identity	Places, associations, networks where the person's capacities would be welcome	How the person can act as a contributing citizen in this place, association, or network.

Prospecting for New Connections in My Community

Use the worksheet on the facing page to summarize your exploration of your learning partner's community for opportunities to get involved in a positive way. Some opportunities will be with family or close friends, like an annual family vacation or Sunday brunch. Some opportunities will be neighborhood activities, like having coffee or eating out. Some opportunities will come from associations like neighborhood watch or a church.

Some opportunities will offer paid or volunteer work or chances to learn. Once you know the sort of connections you are looking for, you can gather leads from many sources. You can…

…walk around and look with fresh eyes

…ask people, especially people who know a lot of other people (if a person doesn't know, ask them if they know someone who might know)

…look on bulletin boards in the supermarket or in church or at the library or at community centers

…look on local internet sites

…look in local newspapers (penny-savers and free papers as well as the main paper).

Put a $ next to opportunities that your learning partner will have to pay for (dues, admission, equipment, etc.).

Circle the two or three opportunities that seem most interesting, put the name and maybe the phone number or e-mail address of a contact person next to these opportunities.

List five positive steps to follow-up on these connections.

-
-
-
-
-

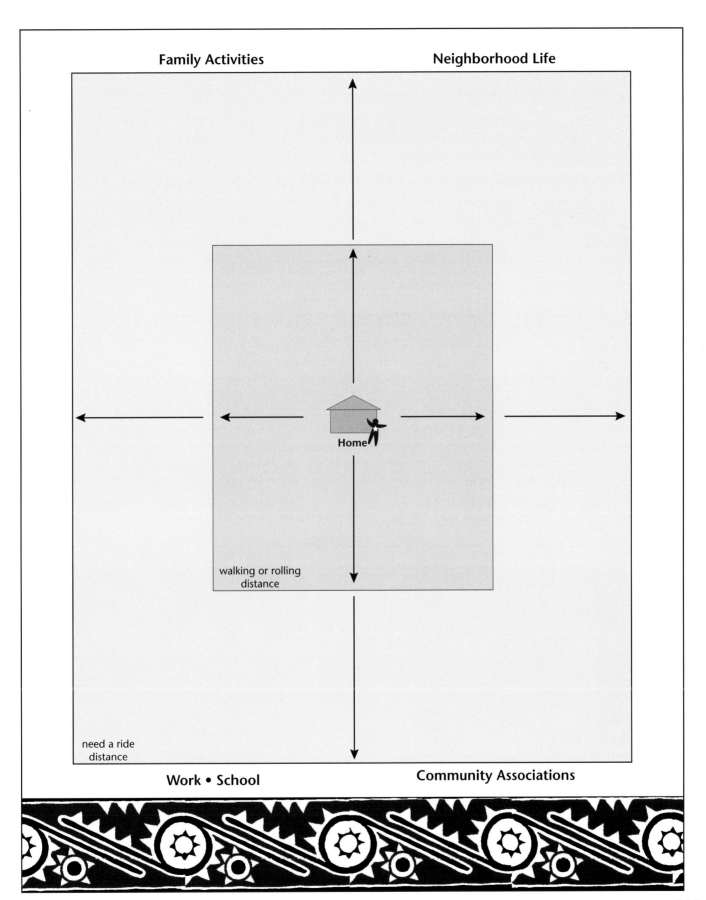

Family Activities

Neighborhood Life

Home

walking or rolling
distance

need a ride
distance

Work • School

Community Associations

Making It Real

Use the worksheet on the facing page to plan the changes to your learning partner's assistance that will make it possible to try new connections. Think about...

- *Do support staff need any new information to make this change work? If so, how will it be communicated?*

- *Do support staff need to use any new skills to make this change work? If so, how will they get the chance to learn them?*

- *What changes are needed in direct support workers' schedules or in other schedules?*

- *How do new people typically join in? Does my learning partner need any accommodation to join? Would my learning partner benefit from someone who is already involved as a sponsor or mentor? If so, how will we recruit this person?*

- *Is any equipment or any particular clothing needed? Are there any fees or expenses?*

- *How will my learning partner get to and from the places involved? How will any necessary arrangements be made?*

- *Are there any particular accessibility requirements? What needs to be done to meet them?*

- *Does my learning partner have any particular communication requirements? What needs to be done to meet them?*

- *Are there any particular safety or health requirements? What needs to be done to meet them?*

Remember some things are easy to predict, like the need for an accessible toilet. Other things are very hard to predict, like how someone will react in a new environment. For the important unpredictable's, it's more important to plan for careful observation and thoughtful reaction by a responsible person who knows and trusts your learning partner than to try to make detailed plans for anything that could possibly happen. (Sometimes it's a good idea to build up a relationship by trying some lower stress new things together before jumping in to a new opportunity.)

Be sure that the responsible people sign-up to these changes.

Note the times that will be most affected by these changes here:

	S	M	T	W	T	F	S
AM							
PM							
Evening							

What change?	Who is Responsible?	First Steps & Completion Dates
		<ul><li></li><li></li><li></li></ul>
		<ul><li></li><li></li><li></li></ul>
		<ul><li></li><li></li><li></li></ul>
		<ul><li></li><li></li><li></li></ul>
		<ul><li></li><li></li><li></li></ul>
		<ul><li></li><li></li><li></li></ul>

Telling the Story

Complete each cycle of learning by creating new connections by reflecting on these questions with your learning partner and your learning buddy:

- *What has happened so far? What has been accomplished?*
- *What are the most important lessons from this experience? What worked?*
- *What is next?*

You can tell the story in many ways...

Make a "one-thing-leads-to-another tree" that illustrates a chain of changes (story on page 131).

Do a powerpoint presentation that illustrates what happened with photographs. Select music that says something important about the experience (story on page 71).

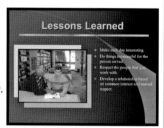

Make a story-board. (see p. 86)

Make and explain a quilt that celebrates what you have accomplished together. Write a poem to go along with the quilt (story and poem on page 76).

Write a song (see page 20).

Anything else your imagination can create to tell the story.

Use the space on the next page to outline the story of what has happened so far, what you have learned, and what's next.

@ Internet Resources

Capacity Works. Books on person-centred work. Posters. Cards. **www.capacityworks.com**

Inclusion Press. Books and tapes on inclusion, person-centered work, community building, restorative justice. **www.inclusion.com**

The Center on Human Policy. Free downloadable resources. Supports for community living. Policy and law. Promising practices. Edited links to many other organizations and resources. **http://thechp.syr.edu**

The National Alliance for Direct Support Professionals. Code of ethics. Action to improve working conditions. Best practices. Newsletters. **www.nadsp.org**

Diverse-City Press. Books, videos, tapes on understanding disability, sexuality, self-esteem, mental health issues. **www.diverse-city.com**

David Pitonyak. Understanding and supporting people with difficult behavior. Positive practices at work. Dealing with the difficulties of caring. **www.dimagine.com**

Mayer Shevin. Positive supports for people with behavioral difficulties. Assistance with Communication. Strategies for preventing abuse. **www.shevin.org**

Breaking the Barriers. Communication for people who don't use spoken words. **www.breaking-the-barriers.org**

TASH International membership organization. Inclusion. Community Living. Employment. Positive Behavior Supports. Communication rights. **www.tash.org**

INCLUSION PRESS ORDER FORM

24 Thorne Crescent, Toronto, ON Canada M6H 2S5
Tel: 416-658-5363 Fax: 416-658-5067
E-mail: inclusionpress@inclusion.com   WEB: http://www.inclusion.com

Inclusion SPECIAL PACKS...

		Copies	Total
The Community PACK	$40 + $7 shipping/pack	____	____
- Members of Each Other & Celebrating the Ordinary - 2 books - John O'Brien & Connie Lyle O'Brien			
The Education Book PACK	$40 + $7 shipping/pack	____	____
- Inclusion: Recent Research & Inclusion: How To - 2 Books - Gary Bunch			
Friendship PACK (1 book + DVD or Video)	$60 + $10 shipping/pack	____	____
- [Friendship DVD/Video + From Behind the Piano/What's Really Worth Doing]			
Inclusion Classics Book PACK [Action for Inclusion + Inclusion Papers]	$30 + $7 shipping/pack	____	____
Inclusion Classics DVD PACK (DVD format or video)	$90 + $12 shipping/pack	____	____
- [With a Little Help from My Friends + Kids Belong Together]			
PATH in ACTION PACK (DVD format, video also available)	$150 + $15 shipping/pack	____	____
- 2 PATH Training "Videos" (DVD) [PATH in Action + PATH Training + the PATH Workbook]			
Petroglyphs PACK - Book & Video on Inclusion in High Schools - from UNH	$60 + $10 shipping/pack	____	____
PlayFair Teams Kit - (Teacher's book, Advocate's book , Intro CD, 2 posters)	$65 + $10 shipping/pack	____	____
When Spider Webs Unite PACK - Shafik Asante - Book and DVD/Video	$80 + $10 shipping/pack	____	____

Books

		Copies	Total
ABCD:When People Care Enough to Act (ABCD in Action.Green)	$25 + $5 /1st copy shipping	____	____
Action for Inclusion - Classic on Inclusion	$20 + $5 /1st copy shipping	____	____
All My Life's a Circle Expanded Edition- Circles, MAPS & PATH	$20 + $5 /1st copy shipping	____	____
The All Star Company - Team Building by Nick Marsh	$20 + $5 /1st copy shipping	____	____
The Careless Society - John McKnight	$25 + $5 /1st copy shipping	____	____
Celebrating the Ordinary O'Brien, O'Brien & Jacob	$25 + $5 /1st copy shipping	____	____
Circle of Friends by Bob & Martha Perske	$25 + $5 /1st copy shipping	____	____
Circles of Adults - Colin Newton & Derek Wilson (UK)	$30 + $5 /1st copy shipping	____	____
Community Lost & Found Arthur Lockhart & Michael Clarke	$25 + $5 /1st copy shipping	____	____
Creating Circles of Friends - Colin Newton & Derek Wilson (UK)	$25 + $5 /1st copy shipping	____	____
Do You Hear What I Hear? - Janice Fialka & Karen Mikus	$15 + $5 /1st copy shipping	____	____
Dream Catchers & Dolphins Marsha Forest and Jack Pearpoint	$20 + $5 /1st copy shipping	____	____
Each Belongs -Jim Hansen with Leyden, Bunch, Pearpoint (book with CD)	$30 + $5 /1st copy shipping	____	____
Finding Meaning in the Work - (CD + Manual/Curriculum) (O'Briens)	$195 + $8 shipping /1st copy	____	____
Free to Fly - A Story of Manic Depression , Caroline Fei-Yeng Kwok	$25 + $5 /1st copy shipping	____	____
From Behind the Piano - by Jack Pearpoint & **What's Really Worth Doing** by Judith Snow			
- **Now in ONE Book**	$20 + $5 /1st copy shipping	____	____
Hints for Graphic Facilitators - Jack Pearpoint	$25 + $5 /1st copy shipping	____	____
The Inclusion Papers - Strategies & Stories	$20 + $5 /1st copy shipping	____	____
Inclusion: How To Essential Classroom Strategies - Gary Bunch	$25+ $5 /1st copy shipping	____	____
Inclusion: Recent Research G. Bunch & A. Valeo	$25 + $5 /1st copy shipping	____	____
Incurably Human Micheline Mason	$20 + $5 /1st copy shipping	____	____
It Matters - Lessons from my Son - Janice Fialka	$15 + $5 /1st copy shipping	____	____
Kids, Disabilities Regular Classrooms Gary Bunch	$20 + $5 /1st copy shipping	____	____
Lessons for Inclusion Curriculum Ideas for Inclusion in Elementary Schools	$20 + $5 /1st copy shipping	____	____
A Little Book About Person Centered Planning	$20 + $5 /1st copy shipping	____	____
John O'Brien & Connie Lyle O'Brien with Forest, Lovett, Mount, Pearpoint, Smull, Snow, and Strully			
Make a Difference: Direct Support Guidebook (J. O'Brien & B. Mount)	$25 + $5 shipping /1st copy	____	____
Make a Difference: Leader's Resource Kit (Instructor's book + CD)	$30 + $5 shipping /1st copy	____	____
Make a Difference: Learning Journey Booklet (Packet of 10)	$20 + $5 shipping /1st set	____	____
MAPS & PATH: A Workbook for Facilitators			
John O'Brien & Jack Pearpoint - New Edition 2007	$25 + $5 /1st copy shipping	____	____
Members of Each Other John O'Brien & Connie Lyle O'Brien	$25 + $5 /1st copy shipping	____	____
One Candle Power - Cathy Ludlum & Communitas	$25 + $5 /1st copy shipping	____	____
PATH Workbook - 2nd Edition Planning Positive Possible Futures	$20 + $5 /1st copy shipping	____	____
Perske - Pencil Portraits 1971-1990	$30 + $5 /1st copy shipping	____	____
Petroglyphs - Inclusion in High School from UNH	$20 + $5 /1st copy shipping	____	____
PlayFair Teams: A Manual for Teacher Advisors	$15 + $5 /1st copy shipping	____	____
PlayFair Teams: A Community Advocate's Manual	$15 + $5 /1st copy shipping	____	____
Reflections on Inclusive Education - Fr. Patrick Mackan C.R.	$15 + $5 /1st copy shipping	____	____
Remembering the Soul of Our Work John OBrien & C. Lyle-O'Brien	$20 + $5 /1st copy shipping	____	____
Restorative Justice Art Lockhart, Lynn Zammit, Randy Charboneau	$25 + $5 /1st copy shipping	____	____
Seeing the Charade Carole Tashie and Team	$25 + $5 /1st copy shipping	____	____

Item	Price		
Sharing Community Options: Lisa Mills & Gary Messinger	$25 + $5 /1st copy shipping	____	_____
Supporting Learners with Intellectual Challenge Gary Bunch	$15 + $5 /1st copy shipping	____	_____
Voices of Experience: Implementing Person-Centered Planning			
Editors: John O'Brien & Connie Lyle O'Brien	$25 + $5 /1st copy shipping	____	_____
Waddie Welcome & the Beloved Community T.Kohler & S.Earl	$25 + $5 /1st copy shipping	____	_____
When Spider Webs Unite Community & Inclusion- Shafik Asante	$20 + $5 /1st copy shipping	____	_____
Yes! She Knows She's Here Nicola Schaefer's Book about Kathrine	$20 + $5 /1st copy shipping	____	_____
Inclusion – Exclusion Poster (18 X 24)	$10 + $5 /1st copy shipping	____	_____
Person Centered Direct Support Foldout (call for bulk rates)	$ 5 + $2 /1st copy shipping	____	_____
Inclusion News in Bulk (box of 100)	$50 – includes shipping in NA	____	_____

MEDIA: DVDs • CD-ROMs • Videos

Item	Price		
ABCD in ACTION -DVD-Mike Green, Henry Moore & John McKnight (includes book)	$150 + $8 shipping /1st copy	____	_____
Dream Catchers (Dreams & Circles)	$55 + $8 shipping /1st copy	____	_____
EVERYONE Has a GIFT J McKnight - Building Communities of Capacity -DVD/Video	$75 + $8 shipping /1st copy	____	_____
Finding Meaning in the Work - (CD + Manual/Curriculum) (O'Briens)	$195 + $8 shipping /1st copy	____	_____
Friendship DVD/Video Judith, Marsha & Jack on Friendship	$55 + $8 shipping /1st copy	____	_____
The Inclusion Classics - DVD (2 classic inclusion videos on DVD/Video)	$90 + $8 shipping /1st copy	____	_____
Kids Belong Together - MAPS & Circles (DVD/Video)	$55 + $8 shipping /1st copy	____	_____
Make a Difference: Leader's Resource Kit (Instructor's book + CD)	$30 + $5 shipping /1st copy	____	_____
The MAPS Collection - DVD (2 MAPS Training videos on DVD)	$150 + $8 shipping /1st copy	____	_____
Miller's MAP - MAPS in Action (DVD/Video)	$55 + $8 shipping /1st copy	____	_____
My Life, My Choice - DVD (7 stories of adults with full lives)	$150 + $8 shipping /1st copy	____	_____
NEW MAPS TRAINING DVD (Shafik//MAPS Process/Judith on Dreaming) DVD/Video	$75 + $8 shipping /1st copy	____	_____
The PATH Collection - DVD (2 PATH Training videos on DVD)	$150 + $8 shipping /1st copy	____	_____
PATH Demo Video Univ of Dayton Ohio - Video of Workshop on PATH	$55 + $8 shipping /1st copy	____	_____
PATH IN ACTION Working with Groups -Training DVD/Video for Path with Groups	$100 + $8 shipping /1st copy	____	_____
PATH TRAINING DVD Intro Training DVD/Video - An Individual Path {Joe's Path}	$75 + $8 shipping /1st copy	____	_____
Person Centered Direct Support - CD - 4 minute video & powerpoint	$25 + $8 shipping /1st copy	____	_____
Petroglyphs Video Companion to Petroglyphs Book - **Packaged with book**	$60 + $8 shipping /1st copy	____	_____
PlayFair Teams CD-ROM An introduction to PlayFair Teams	$50 + $8 shipping /1st copy	____	_____
ReDiscovering MAPS Charting Your Journey - MAPS training DVD/Video	$100 + $8 shipping /1st copy	____	_____
Together We're Better (3 DVDs) Staff Development Kit	$175 + $12 shipping	____	_____
TOOLS for CHANGE - The CD-Rom for Person Centred Planning		____	_____
Pricing is dependent on a licensing agreement. Call us. Interative CD - 70 Tools, 180 overheads, 18 articles, 30 video clips, 4 slide shows.			
When Spider Webs Unite - DVD/Video Shafik Asante in Action	$75 + $8 /1st copy shipping	____	_____
With a Little Help from My Friends The Classic on Circles & MAPS - DVD/Video	$55 + $8 shipping /1st copy	____	_____

Plus applicable taxes (variable)

GRAND TOTAL $===========

*Join us at the **Toronto Summer Institute***
July in Toronto
Inclusion • Community • Diversity
www.inclusion.com

Training Events:
Made to measure!
PATH & Maps; Make a Difference
Contact: inclusionpress@inclusion.com

Credit Cards on the Net (secure), Cheques,
Money Orders, Purchase Orders
• **Prices subject to change without notice.**
Shipping prices for North America only.
Elsewhere by quote.
• **Shipping: Books: $5 for 1st + $2/copy;**
Videos: $8 for 1st+ $4/copy. OR 15% of
total order cost - which ever is less.

New Resources

• **ABCD in Action** - DVD & Book -When People Care Enough to Act
• **My Life My Choice** - DVD - Seven Adults living full lives in the community
• **Make a Difference** - book; Leaders Guide, Work Booklets
• **Each Belongs** - book & CD - The 1st Inclusive School Board ever!
• **PlayFair Teams** - 2 books, DVD + Posters - blended teams in schools.
• **Find Meaning in the Work** - CD & Manual/Curriculum - presentation ready!
• **Free to Fly** - A Story of Manic Depression - Caroline Fei-Yeng Kwok
• **Supporting Learners with Intellectual Challenge** -teacher resources
• **Incurably Human** - Micheline Mason - advocacy, poetry, rights - England & us
• **Seeing the Charade** - Carole Tashie et al - inclusion in schools - just do it!
• **Sharing Community** - Stories of Community Membership how we are doing it....

Name: _____
Organization:_____
Address:_____
City: _____
Prov/State _____ Post Code/ZIP _____
Wk Phone _____ Cheque Enclosed _____
Hm Phone _____ Fax _____
E-Mail _____ Web Page:_____

INCLUSION PRESS ORDER FORM

24 Thorne Crescent, Toronto, ON Canada M6H 2S5
Tel: 416-658-5363 Fax: 416-658-5067
E-mail: inclusionpress@inclusion.com   WEB: http://www.inclusion.com

Inclusion SPECIAL PACKS...

The Community PACK $40 + $7 shipping/pack   ____ _____
    - Members of Each Other & Celebrating the Ordinary - 2 books - John O'Brien & Connie Lyle O'Brien

The Education Book PACK $40 + $7 shipping/pack   ____ _____
    - Inclusion: Recent Research & Inclusion: How To - 2 Books - Gary Bunch

Friendship PACK (1 book + DVD or Video) $60 + $10 shipping/pack   ____ _____
    - [Friendship DVD/Video + From Behind the Piano/What's Really Worth Doing]

Inclusion Classics Book PACK [Action for Inclusion + Inclusion Papers] $30 + $7 shipping/pack ____ _____

Inclusion Classics DVD PACK (DVD format or video) $90 + $12 shipping/pack   ____ _____
    - [With a Little Help from My Friends + Kids Belong Together]

PATH in ACTION PACK (DVD format, video also available) $150 + $15 shipping/pack   ____ _____
    - 2 PATH Training "Videos" (DVD) [PATH in Action + PATH Training + the PATH Workbook]

Petroglyphs PACK - Book & Video on Inclusion in High Schools - from UNH $60 + $10 shipping/pack ____ _____

PlayFair Teams Kit - (Teacher's book, Advocate's book , Intro CD, 2 posters) $65 + $10 shipping/pack ____ _____

When Spider Webs Unite PACK - Shafik Asante - Book and DVD/Video $80 + $10 shipping/pack ____ _____

Books   Copies Total

ABCD:When People Care Enough to Act (ABCD in Action.Green)	$25 + $5 /1st copy shipping	____ _____
Action for Inclusion - Classic on Inclusion	$20 + $5 /1st copy shipping	____ _____
All My Life's a Circle Expanded Edition- Circles, MAPS & PATH	$20 + $5 /1st copy shipping	____ _____
The All Star Company - Team Building by Nick Marsh	$20 + $5 /1st copy shipping	____ _____
The Careless Society - John McKnight	$25 + $5 /1st copy shipping	____ _____
Celebrating the Ordinary O'Brien, O'Brien & Jacob	$25 + $5 /1st copy shipping	____ _____
Circle of Friends by Bob & Martha Perske	$25 + $5 /1st copy shipping	____ _____
Circles of Adults - Colin Newton & Derek Wilson (UK)	$30 + $5 /1st copy shipping	____ _____
Community Lost & Found Arthur Lockhart & Michael Clarke	$25 + $5 /1st copy shipping	____ _____
Creating Circles of Friends - Colin Newton & Derek Wilson (UK)	$25 + $5 /1st copy shipping	____ _____
Do You Hear What I Hear? - Janice Fialka & Karen Mikus	$15 + $5 /1st copy shipping	____ _____
Dream Catchers & Dolphins Marsha Forest and Jack Pearpoint	$20 + $5 /1st copy shipping	____ _____
Each Belongs -Jim Hansen with Leyden, Bunch, Pearpoint (book with CD)	$30 + $5 /1st copy shipping	____ _____
Finding Meaning in the Work - (CD + Manual/Curriculum) (O'Briens)	$195 + $8 shipping /1st copy	____ _____
Free to Fly - A Story of Manic Depression , Caroline Fei-Yeng Kwok	$25 + $5 /1st copy shipping	____ _____
From Behind the Piano - by Jack Pearpoint & **What's Really Worth Doing** by Judith Snow - Now in ONE Book	$20 + $5 /1st copy shipping	____ _____
Hints for Graphic Facilitators - Jack Pearpoint	$25 + $5 /1st copy shipping	____ _____
The Inclusion Papers - Strategies & Stories	$20 + $5 /1st copy shipping	____ _____
Inclusion: How To Essential Classroom Strategies - Gary Bunch	$25+ $5 /1st copy shipping	____ _____
Inclusion: Recent Research G. Bunch & A. Valeo	$25 + $5 /1st copy shipping	____ _____
Incurably Human Micheline Mason	$20 + $5 /1st copy shipping	____ _____
It Matters - Lessons from my Son - Janice Fialka	$15 + $5 /1st copy shipping	____ _____
Kids, Disabilities Regular Classrooms Gary Bunch	$20 + $5 /1st copy shipping	____ _____
Lessons for Inclusion Curriculum Ideas for Inclusion in Elementary Schools	$20 + $5 /1st copy shipping	____ _____
A Little Book About Person Centered Planning John O'Brien & Connie Lyle O'Brien with Forest, Lovett, Mount, Pearpoint, Smull, Snow, and Strully	$20 + $5 /1st copy shipping	____ _____
Make a Difference: Direct Support Guidebook (J. O'Brien & B. Mount)	$25 + $5 shipping /1st copy	____ _____
Make a Difference: Leader's Resource Kit (Instructor's book + CD)	$30 + $5 shipping /1st copy	____ _____
Make a Difference: Learning Journey Booklet (Packet of 10)	$20 + $5 shipping /1st set	____ _____
MAPS & PATH: A Workbook for Facilitators John O'Brien & Jack Pearpoint - New Edition 2007	$25 + $5 /1st copy shipping	____ _____
Members of Each Other John O'Brien & Connie Lyle O'Brien	$25 + $5 /1st copy shipping	____ _____
One Candle Power - Cathy Ludlum & Communitas	$25 + $5 /1st copy shipping	____ _____
PATH Workbook - 2nd Edition Planning Positive Possible Futures	$20 + $5 /1st copy shipping	____ _____
Perske - Pencil Portraits 1971-1990	$30 + $5 /1st copy shipping	____ _____
Petroglyphs - Inclusion in High School from UNH	$20 + $5 /1st copy shipping	____ _____
PlayFair Teams: A Manual for Teacher Advisors	$15 + $5 /1st copy shipping	____ _____
PlayFair Teams: A Community Advocate's Manual	$15 + $5 /1st copy shipping	____ _____
Reflections on Inclusive Education - Fr. Patrick Mackan C.R.	$15 + $5 /1st copy shipping	____ _____
Remembering the Soul of Our Work John OBrien & C. Lyle-O'Brien	$20 + $5 /1st copy shipping	____ _____
Restorative Justice Art Lockhart, Lynn Zammit, Randy Charboneau	$25 + $5 /1st copy shipping	____ _____
Seeing the Charade Carole Tashie and Team	$25 + $5 /1st copy shipping	

Sharing Community Options: Lisa Mills & Gary Messinger	$25 + $5 /1st copy shipping	____ _____
Supporting Learners with Intellectual Challenge Gary Bunch	$15 + $5 /1st copy shipping	____ _____
Voices of Experience: Implementing Person-Centered Planning		
Editors: John O'Brien & Connie Lyle O'Brien	$25 + $5 /1st copy shipping	____ _____
Waddie Welcome & the Beloved Community T.Kohler & S.Earl	$25 + $5 /1st copy shipping	____ _____
When Spider Webs Unite Community & Inclusion- Shafik Asante	$20 + $5 /1st copy shipping	____ _____
Yes! She Knows She's Here Nicola Schaefer's Book about Kathrine	$20 + $5 /1st copy shipping	____ _____
Inclusion – Exclusion Poster (18 X 24)	$10 + $5 /1st copy shipping	____ _____
Person Centered Direct Support Foldout (call for bulk rates)	$ 5 + $2 /1st copy shipping	____ _____
Inclusion News in Bulk (box of 100)	$50 – includes shipping in NA	____ _____

MEDIA: DVDs • CD-ROMs • Videos

ABCD in ACTION -DVD-Mike Green, Henry Moore & John McKnight (includes book)	$150 + $8 shipping /1st copy	____ _____
Dream Catchers (Dreams & Circles)	$55 + $8 shipping /1st copy	____ _____
EVERYONE Has a GIFT J McKnight - Building Communities of Capacity -DVD/Video	$75 + $8 shipping /1st copy	____ _____
Finding Meaning in the Work - (CD + Manual/Curriculum) (O'Briens)	$195 + $8 shipping /1st copy	____ _____
Friendship DVD/Video Judith, Marsha & Jack on Friendship	$55 + $8 shipping /1st copy	____ _____
The Inclusion Classics - DVD (2 classic inclusion videos on DVD/Video)	$90 + $8 shipping /1st copy	____ _____
Kids Belong Together - MAPS & Circles (DVD/Video)	$55 + $8 shipping /1st copy	____ _____
Make a Difference: Leader's Resource Kit (Instructor's book + CD)	$30 + $5 shipping /1st copy	____ _____
The MAPS Collection - DVD (2 MAPS Training videos on DVD)	$150 + $8 shipping /1st copy	____ _____
Miller's MAP - MAPS in Action (DVD/Video)	$55 + $8 shipping /1st copy	____ _____
My Life, My Choice - DVD (7 stories of adults with full lives)	$150 + $8 shipping /1st copy	____ _____
NEW MAPS TRAINING DVD (Shafik//MAPS Process/Judith on Dreaming) DVD/Video	$75 + $8 shipping /1st copy	____ _____
The PATH Collection - DVD (2 PATH Training videos on DVD)	$150 + $8 shipping /1st copy	____ _____
PATH Demo Video Univ of Dayton Ohio - Video of Workshop on PATH	$55 + $8 shipping /1st copy	____ _____
PATH IN ACTION Working with Groups -Training DVD/Video for Path with Groups	$100 + $8 shipping /1st copy	____ _____
PATH TRAINING DVD Intro Training DVD/Video - An Individual Path {Joe's Path}	$75 + $8 shipping /1st copy	____ _____
Person Centered Direct Support - CD - 4 minute video & powerpoint	$25 + $8 shipping /1st copy	____ _____
Petroglyphs Video Companion to Petroglyphs Book - **Packaged with book**	$60 + $8 shipping /1st copy	____ _____
PlayFair Teams CD-ROM An introduction to PlayFair Teams	$50 + $8 shipping /1st copy	____ _____
ReDiscovering MAPS Charting Your Journey - MAPS training DVD/Video	$100 + $8 shipping /1st copy	____ _____
Together We're Better (3 DVDs) Staff Development Kit	$175 + $12 shipping	____ _____
TOOLS for CHANGE - The CD-Rom for Person Centred Planning		____ _____
Pricing is dependent on a licensing agreement. Call us. Interative CD - 70 Tools, 180 overheads, 18 articles, 30 video clips, 4 slide shows.		
When Spider Webs Unite - DVD/Video Shafik Asante in Action	$75 + $8 /1st copy shipping	____ _____
With a Little Help from My Friends The Classic on Circles & MAPS - DVD/Video	$55 + $8 shipping /1st copy	____ _____

Plus applicable taxes (variable)

GRAND TOTAL $===========

---

*Join us at the **Toronto Summer Institute***
July in Toronto
Inclusion • Community • Diversity
www.inclusion.com

Training Events:
Made to measure!
PATH & Maps; Make a Difference
Contact: inclusionpress@inclusion.com

Credit Cards on the Net (secure), Cheques,
Money Orders, Purchase Orders
• **Prices subject to change without notice.**
Shipping prices for North America only.
Elsewhere by quote.
• **Shipping: Books: $5 for 1st + $2/copy;**
Videos: $8 for 1st+ $4/copy. OR 15% of
total order cost - which ever is less.

Tools for Change

CD - Tools for
Person Centered Planning

New Resources

• **ABCD in Action** - DVD & Book -When People Care Enough to Act
• **My Life My Choice** - DVD - Seven Adults living full lives in the community
• **Make a Difference** - book; Leaders Guide, Work Booklets
• **Each Belongs** - book & CD - The 1st Inclusive School Board ever!
• **PlayFair Teams** - 2 books, DVD + Posters - blended teams in schools.
• **Find Meaning in the Work** - CD & Manual/Curriculum - presentation ready!
• **Free to Fly** - A Story of Manic Depression - Caroline Fei-Yeng Kwok
• **Supporting Learners with Intellectual Challenge** -teacher resources
• **Incurably Human** - Micheline Mason - advocacy, poetry, rights - England & us
• **Seeing the Charade** - Carole Tashie et al - inclusion in schools - just do it!
• **Sharing Community** - Stories of Community Membership how we are doing it....

Name: _____
Organization:_____
Address:_____
City: _____
Prov/State _____ Post Code/ZIP _____
Wk Phone _____ Cheque Enclosed _____
Hm Phone _____ Fax _____
E-Mail _____ Web Page:_____